Snake Eyes

Books by Edwin Silberstang

FICTION

Rapt in Glory
Nightmare of the Dark
Sweet Land of Liberty
Losers Weepers
Snake Eyes

NONFICTION

Playboy's Book of Games
Las Vegas, An Insiders' Guide
Play Bridge Tonight
Play Chess Tonight
Play Pinochle Tonight
Smart Casino Play
Smart Keno Play
Poker Made Playable

Snake
Eyes

EDWIN SILBERSTANG

TC

Thomas Congdon Books

E. P. Dutton | New York

For Nellie Hill, Molly Pratt, and Diane Sampson

Lines from "Cape Hatteras" from *The Bridge,* by Hart Crane. Reprinted from *The Complete Poems and Selected Letters and Prose of Hart Crane,* edited by Brom Weber. Reprinted by permission of Liveright Publishing Corporation. Copyright 1933, © 1958, 1966 by Liveright Publishing Corporation.

Library of Congress Cataloging in Publication Data
Silberstang, Edwin, 1930–
Snake eyes.
"Thomas Congdon books."
I. Title.
PZ4.S5718Sn [PS3569.I415] 813'.5'4 77-23856
ISBN: 0-525-20625-6

Published simultaneously in Canada by Clarke, Irwin & Company Limited, Toronto and Vancouver

10 9 8 7 6 5 4 3 2 1
First edition

Tuesday

1

Dream cancels dream in this new realm of fact.
From which we wake into the dream of act.

Hart Crane

While Steinberg was walking past the blackjack pit at the El Capitan, he heard his name called. He looked around and saw Diane in the small lounge that was slightly elevated above the casino floor. She was sitting alone at a table near the rail.

"Don," said Diane as he came to the table, "how about a drink with me?"

Steinberg sat down.

"Were you going to play?" she asked.

"No, just walking around. I don't play here that much anymore since they put in the four-deck games."

"One deck, four decks, they're all the same to me. Anyway, I like this place, you know? They leave you alone here. In most of the Strip casinos, if some girl is sitting alone, next thing you know a security guard is rousting her. They think any girl alone is a hooker."

"Well, you're no hooker."

"Just a little chip hustling is all," Diane said. "You'd be surprised at the number of guys who just want a woman

5

around when they gamble, somebody to gamble along with them. And if they want to share their winnings, well, what's wrong with that?"

"Nothing's wrong with that," Don said.

"But you don't need a woman when you gamble, do you, Don?"

"No," he said, smiling, "not then. But I haven't seen you at the El Capitan lately. What brings you here to-night?"

"One of my girlfriends called me. She's supposed to meet these two dudes over at the Frontier and bring them over here. But she's late. Probably got only one of them and is playing with the guy."

"How'd she meet them?"

"Oh, you know, recommendations . . . Jesus, Don, if you ask me how I meet these dudes . . . They call up, someone tells them about me, or whatever . . . I don't even know anymore. How about buying me a drink?"

The cocktail waitress came over and Steinberg ordered a Wild Turkey and water for himself, and a Dewar's on the rocks for Diane.

"You look a little down," he told her.

"I am. You see everything, don't you? I am. I am. You know, I was back in Kansas a few weeks ago, visiting my mom and my kid. You know my boy is six years old now. He's a big kid."

Don nodded.

"You want to see a picture of him?"

"OK."

Diane reached into her purse and produced a wallet. She carefully took out a few color pictures of a young boy and passed them along to Steinberg. "Isn't he pretty? You don't have to answer that, Don. But, isn't he?"

"He's a nice-looking boy."

"Blond like me. You know, I used to be blond, right

through high school, but then my hair darkened a little, did you know that?"

"No, I didn't."

Her hair was light brown and long, surrounding her face, which still held the natural beauty of a college girl, with its high color and lean lines. Diane had glistening white teeth and green eyes, and her figure was still as sleek as it had been seven years before, when she had been a cheerleader at Kansas. "That's what happened, it darkened. Where the hell is that drink? And where's Cindy?"

The drinks came a few minutes later. Steinberg peeled off a couple of bills and paid for them, then raised his glass to Diane. "Here's to your kid," he said.

"I'll drink to that, honey." She drained half the glass. "You have any kids, Don?"

"No."

"You ever been married?"

"Once. I told you that when I first met you."

"Jesus, I don't remember asking you. You were married? No shit?"

"Yes."

"I can't picture you being married."

Don stared at his drink, then gulped it down.

"What happened?" she asked.

"What happened? What do you mean, what happened?"

"I mean . . . you're not married now, are you?"

"No."

"You get divorced?"

Steinberg shrugged.

"You don't want to talk about it?" she asked.

"Maybe some other time."

"OK." She looked around. "Don, what do you think? I mean, about my kid. He's been living with my mother since he was born. I ought to have him stay with me. What do you think?"

"I think you should."

"Have him live with me?"

"Yes."

"You really mean that?"

"Yes, I mean everything I say."

She stared at him. "I know you do. I know that, Don. But how can he live with me in Vegas?"

"You know how, Diane. Just fly him out here. What's this, July? July, right? You could check with the schools and have him in school in September."

She continued to stare at him, leaning back in her chair. "Maybe you're right."

"I'm not right or wrong. It's up to you."

They sat silently for a few minutes. Then Diane finished her drink and pushed the glass away. "Don, would you get me another Scotch? I think they water them down. I can't feel them anymore."

He signaled for the waitress, then ordered two more drinks.

"I was just thinking," Diane said, "about the first time I met you . . . where was that?"

"At the Dunes."

"Yes, I sat next to you. I did that on purpose, you know?"

"Did you think you could hustle me?"

"Don . . . Don . . . don't think that. No, I sort of liked the way you looked, the way you were sitting there. And then you were winning so much money. You had your pockets stuffed with casino checks."

"Yes, it was a good win."

"Don, why don't we ever go out and play blackjack together?"

"Maybe we should."

"We should, shouldn't we?"

He nodded.

8

"And why don't you come over to my place? Come over tomorrow. Can you come over tomorrow?"

"When?"

"For supper. I'll cook you supper. I have some fresh salmon. How about it?"

"All right. I'll drop over about seven or so. How's that?"

"Good. I'll cook you a whole meal. I bet you didn't think I could? Right?"

"I know you can do anything." He patted her cheek. The waitress came with the fresh drinks. Don kept his hand on Diane's cheek, then removed it and paid the waitress.

"You ought to get your kid out here," he said, after tasting his drink.

"I'm afraid to, Don."

"There's nothing to be afraid of." He yawned and leaned back in his chair, thinking that he hadn't been getting much sleep lately. He'd been waking at all hours, for some reason, and getting up and dressing and cruising the casinos and the Strip. He could imagine how he looked, with dark circles under his eyes. *I need some sleep,* he told himself, *one good night's sleep.*

Steinberg stretched his legs. He was just under six feet in height, and the jacket he wore was filled out by his wide, sloping shoulders. His frame was wiry and muscular. He had a solid thick neck, which jutted out of his open sports shirt, the only visible indication of his powerful body. His face wasn't handsome, the nose having been broken a couple of times, but his features were regular, and his straight brown hair fell over his forehead.

"What time is it?" Diane asked.

"It's ten to twelve."

"Cindy was supposed to meet me between eleven and

eleven-thirty, and now it's almost midnight. After this drink, I'm going to take off."

"Going home?"

"Yes, you want to come home with me? We could get stoned and you could stay over if you wanted."

"Not tonight, Diane."

She kept her eyes on his face while she drank. "Maybe I won't go home," Diane said. "Maybe I'll do a little playing instead." She put the glass down. "Are you going to play twenty-one?" she asked.

"I don't know. Maybe just cruise the Strip. Maybe go downtown. I don't know."

"You're wasting your time in Vegas, you know that, don't you, Don?"

"I know it better than anyone."

"Why don't you get out?"

"I'll get out soon, but I have my plans."

"What plans?"

"Diane, this is the town to make the bread. I want to make enough to be independent, not to have to take orders from any son of a bitch again in my life."

"Good luck."

"I'll make it, Diane. All I need is a backer."

"You'll get one. I have faith in you, baby, really I do."

They finished their drinks.

"I think I'm going to take off," Don said.

"Where are you going?"

"I don't know. Just take a ride, go up and down the Strip. Just feel like moving along."

"Don, you're worse than me. You're so restless . . ."

He shrugged. They got to their feet, Diane a little unsteadily.

"You want me to give you a lift?" he asked.

"No, I've got the silver bird outside. I'm going to hang

around a little, do some playing. It looks like Cindy's not showing up. Then maybe I'll meet some dude."

"Well, take care, Diane. I'm going to take off."

She put her arms around his waist.

"How about a little kiss goodnight? A little toke?"

Don kissed her on the lips and she moved her tongue against his closed lips.

"Just a toke," she said. "A message from me to you."

He patted her cheek and went down the steps to the casino floor. Diane sat down again and decided to have one more drink before she hit the tables.

2

Steinberg left the El Capitan, heading south on the Strip. He cut into the driveway of Caesars Palace a few minutes later and parked in the huge side lot. Some nights he preferred valet service at the front door, especially if he was carrying a lot of cash.

He walked along the side of the main building and entered the casino. Two couples were standing near the Ah So Bar, chattering about the show they had seen there that night. Steinberg hadn't even noticed who was appearing at Caesars; he rarely paid attention to the shows in Vegas. That was for the tourists when they swarmed here. He had something else on his mind.

He walked down the center aisle, casually watching the action at the blackjack tables. They were crowded, even though it was past midnight. He hated to play a crowded table. In any case, there wasn't a space available.

Steinberg paused at a $100 table and watched the play. A Mexican was betting $1,000 a hand and playing two hands at once, while his wife sat next to him, diamonds sparkling from almost every chubby finger. The Mexican examined the first hand dealt to him, then hit and busted, and the dealer quickly slid the pile of $100 checks into a tray. He busted on the second hand also, as his wife sighed and whispered something into his ear. The Mexican nodded gravely and asked the floorman nearby for a marker.

Just one of those things, thought Steinberg, moving on. He wasn't interested in the game, but in one for himself. With $600 in his pockets, burning a hole there, he wasn't about to get into a $100 game. Maybe someday, but not yet. When he had first come to Vegas, he had stuck to the $1 and $2 games. He'd read all the books on blackjack before leaving the East and, after dealing himself thousands of hands, had worked out his own method of playing the game—complete with an elaborate point count and a right move for every play in every possible situation.

But it was one thing to sit in his room playing with Woolworth chips—where he could pause to take the count and reflect on each move—and it was something else to be at a casino, facing a hostile dealer who snapped the cards at him with blinding speed. Something else altogether.

That's why he avoided the Strip hotels at first and stuck with the downtown casinos, where he'd have the cheap breakfast every morning and then gamble at the tables, never betting more than $2 a hand.

And some of the dealers in these places were really inept. They couldn't add numbers, either the totals of the cards or the payoffs. Sometimes he'd be paid off after busting, and sometimes the dealers were so incompetent that they'd reveal the hole card, the one they'd dealt themselves face down.

But most of the time it was anything but easy. Sometimes the pressure was just too much playing this game. You were always on the line, always betting your own money, and when that money was gone it was gone, and there was no way to replenish it. You couldn't afford to lose that whole stake. If you did you were finished.

Each progression, each move up in his own game, increased the threat to his bankroll. When he had played the $2 tables, he could have a bad streak and lose maybe $50 or $60—a big loss for a $2 game but it couldn't ruin him. But then, after he got the feel of actual play, he moved on to the $5 tables, playing in the large casinos like Caesars and the Dunes. A big loss here was $200, and that was at an absolutely horrible table, when no cards came his way.

Now he was playing the $25 tables, betting up to $100 a hand. It was a hard game, and he could drop $500 or $1,000 in a half hour, playing those limits.

The ball-breaking pressure never stopped. But pressure or not, he had to go on with the games. He had that dream, the same dream that had brought him to Las Vegas—the dream of leaving here with enough money to buy some land for himself, enough money for him to live independently.

It was a dream probably shared by a million losers in this town, Steinberg reflected, as he watched the action at the baccarat pit, but for those losers it was nothing more than a wild fantasy, while for him it was a dream one inch away from reality. Already he had proof that it was possible.

Steinberg had made the long journey out to Vegas with a thousand dollars in cash and a pink '69 Mustang that broke down eight times on the way and finally ended up a smoking wreck two months after his arrival. Now he owned an almost new Pontiac he had paid $3,000 cash for. He had $2,500 in traveler's checks in his apartment. He had been living on his winnings for eight months, all from blackjack.

But he knew he couldn't survive a bad run at the $25

tables. That's why he needed a backer. He needed some-one to bankroll his game, someone he'd split the profits with. It would be a good deal all around, because 99 per-cent of the blackjack players in this town were losers. It was a rough game to beat, no matter what the books said, and unless you played it absolutely right, unless every move was correct, you were going to be destroyed at the game.

Luck evens itself out, he knew, but skill, that was a con-stant. *Yes,* thought Steinberg, *that's the way it is.*

After a couple of drinks at the bar, Steinberg went to a $25 table and put out $500 in bills. There was just one other player at the table, a black dude who was im-peccably dressed in gray and red, and stood while he played. He snapped his fingers as he turned over a black-jack.

"That's the way, baby," he told the dealer, throwing him a $5 check as a tip. "Just keep it up, baby."

"Give me quarters and some dollars," Steinberg told the dealer. He put down $50 as his first bet.

The cards were reshuffled. The black man cut them, bouncing from foot to foot. *The bastard's wired,* thought Steinberg.

The dealer gave Steinberg a 10, 4 for his first hand. The dealer showed a 9 as an upcard. Don hit, got a jack and busted. The black dude turned over another blackjack, and threw another $5 check to the dealer.

That's the way the session went. Steinberg kept busting and the black dude hit a fantastic run. When he was down to $100, Steinberg got up and cashed in. It had taken him exactly twenty minutes to lose $400.

He walked slowly to his car, and then drove back to his apartment on Royal Crest. He walked up one flight to his floor and went inside the apartment. First he turned on the air-conditioner. Then he had a long drink of water from the Sparkletts cooler.

In his bedroom he undressed and crawled into bed. He switched on the radio at the night table and picked up a trucker's station in Denver. Marty Robbins was singing "El Paso."

Steinberg listened with his eyes open, staring at the white textured ceiling. In a couple of hours it would be light. Tomorrow was another day, and maybe things would really start to happen for him. Anything was possible in Vegas. Anything.

That's why he was here.

3

The cab pulled up in front of the El Capitan. Lee Thornton got out, holding onto his attaché case, and waited for the driver to take the suitcase out of the trunk. He was a tall, slim man in his late thirties, with sandy hair going gray at the temples. He had a neat mustache, also sandy, and his light blue eyes were watery. He tipped the cabbie and carried his luggage into the hotel.

At the reservations desk, he waited, fidgeting, as the clerk looked up his name.

"Here it is, sir. Lee Thornton, Chicago."

"That's me."

"Right." The clerk rang a bell, and a bellboy came to the desk. "Room 3025," he told the bellboy, handing him a key. "And good luck, sir. Enjoy your stay at the El Capitan."

"Just get in?" the bellboy asked as they waited for an elevator.

"Yes."

"From LA?"

"Yes. How'd you know?"

"Oh, generally, anyone comes in at this hour, it's from LA."

Thornton glanced sideways, watching the action in the casino. All that action. He got into the elevator when it arrived and rode up to the third floor in silence. The room was all the way down the corridor. He thought, *this is a bitch of a walk to take every time I go to my room,* but he didn't complain to the bellboy. There was no use doing that. After the luggage was set up, the lights turned on, the air-conditioner adjusted, he tipped the boy a buck and took off his jacket.

Thornton looked at his watch. Almost one o'clock in the morning. God damn, a completely wasted day, first flying to LA, then coming here, but how the hell could he have done it otherwise? You just couldn't change stops in midair.

He thought of his wife at the airport in Chicago, kissing him goodbye for his long trip to California, allegedly to look over a real-estate deal and to sign up a new client. He wondered if she suspected where he really was. No, she didn't know about that side of his life. Neither did her father, thank God for that. Her father was the senior partner in his law firm.

Marry the boss's daughter and live the American dream, he thought wryly, taking off his tie. There wasn't much time left before the swing shift in the casino was over, and he couldn't afford the luxury of wasting a few minutes with a hot shower, so he washed off the dirt and sweat from his hands and face as best he could. That done, he left the room.

Then he remembered his attaché case. Jesus, his head was really up his ass this morning. That long flight, the time difference. It was close to three o'clock Chicago time. No wonder.

Thornton went back into his room and opened the case,

taking out several envelopes. They didn't fit into his trousers pockets, so he put on his tie and jacket again, and stuffed in the envelopes. They filled up all the pockets and made bulges.

He was a little nervous about the long walk down the deserted corridor and the empty elevator ride to the lobby, but the El Capitan was the place for him to stay. This was where the real action would be for him, and once he deposited the money he'd breathe easier.

After entering the casino, he headed directly for the cashier's cage in the rear, pausing on the way to look over the dealers at the blackjack tables. Sure enough, Teddy was dealing.

He had to wait on line at the cage while a player cashed in a couple of nickel chips. The player looked like a loser, a big loser. He had that drawn, gray, beaten look, the look all losers have—the shocked and unbelieving look of having been taken at the tables for all they're worth.

How well he himself knew that feeling. He'd ridden on every treadmill of defeat—the racetrack, baseball, whatever he could put a bet on. Thornton grimaced at the memory of all those bets down the drain, losing, losing, losing. He didn't even want to think about it anymore, but how could you stop thinking? That was the real tragedy of life, he reflected, the fact that you couldn't turn your mind off, unless you put a bullet through the brain. There was no other way to cut the switch.

Finally he was at the window. He asked for a safe-deposit box and quickly put all but one of the envelopes into it. He returned the box to the cashier and slipped the key into his wallet.

He left the cage and walked rapidly across the casino floor to the blackjack pit. There was Teddy, at a $25 table, dealing to a lone player. Thornton sat down, took out $1,000 in cash, and dropped it on the table. Teddy picked the money up, spreading the bills as he counted them in front of the tray.

"Change a thousand," the dealer yelled, to catch the attention of the floorman, who came over to watch the action.

"How do you want them?" Teddy asked Thornton.

"Greens and blacks. About half and half."

Thornton's first bet was $200, which he won. He had a fairly good run, but Teddy was relieved by a new dealer, and it was all over.

The new shift had come on, the graveyard shift, and a whole row of dealers were moving to the tables. Thornton decided to cash in. He had won $800 in his short effort at the table, not too much, but not bad. And the cards spoke for themselves. Not once did he need a signal from Teddy.

In the men's room he took a leak, then stood by the mirror combing his hair. Teddy came in and washed his hands, standing next to him.

"Mr. Thornton," said the dealer, looking at Thornton's face through the mirror, "call me later. In the morning, about ten."

"What's up?"

"I got to speak to you then. It's important. Call me."

The dealer walked out of the men's room. Thornton dropped a quarter tip for the attendant and walked out into the casino, troubled. What was this—calling Teddy in the morning? What was it all about?

The whole purpose of this trip was to contact Teddy, to play at his table, to win money there. And now this. Thornton knew, with his lawyer's mind, that the tone of Teddy's voice meant no good. Something was going on. Maybe Teddy had been found out or warned, or something really bad was about to happen.

No sense in thinking about it, in guessing. He headed for the craps pit. At the one crap game open, he removed

$3,000 from the envelope and laid it on the table, asking the dealer for greens and blacks. The money was passed to the boxman, who counted the cash and looked up at him with owlish eyes magnified behind thick lenses.

Thornton piled the casino checks in the rails in front of him, waiting for the dice to be thrown. The shooter was in the middle of a point, the white side of the disk resting on 6 among the place numbers. He could make a bet now, but he told himself to be patient, to wait for the come-out roll.

All the players at the table were men, except for a strikingly handsome woman two places down, separated from Thornton by a fat player smoking a foul cigar. The shooter's next roll was a 7, and, along with a few others, the fat man pushed away from the table, fleeing from the cold dice.

Thornton moved over one place and brought his checks with him. Now he had a better look at the woman. She was just his type, with long legs and a slim figure. And he was stirred by her perfume. He pictured his wife, who, after eight years of marriage was getting heavy and sagging.

"New shooter coming out," announced the stickman, and the players got down their bets. But Thornton, who had been thinking of his wife, was still in a daze, and had no money on the layout as the dice flew his way.

"Three, craps, loser on the pass line, pay don't-pass, pay the field," cried the stickman, and the dealers quickly gathered up the losing bets.

"Shit," said the woman next to him.

"Excuse me?" said Thornton, taking two black checks and placing them on the pass line.

"I said, shit. The dice are ice cold."

"Well, things change. It could be our turn now." He breathed in deeply, smelling her, the mixture of perfume, alcohol, and sweat. He could hardly take his eyes off her body, but he did stop for a moment to see the shooter getting the dice again. He was at the opposite end of the table, a beady-eyed man wearing a cap.

The roller picked up the dice and turned them in his hand till he found the combination he was looking for, then he blew on the dice, and threw them with tremendous force against the other end of the table. One of the dice popped up, off the table, and hit Thornton in the chest, then dropped onto the rails.

"No roll," said the stickman. Thornton handed the die back to the dealer.

New dice were moved to the shooter, who picked out a pair and again went through the ritual of turning them for a secret combination. *This guy is going to make me lose,* thought Thornton, *all this turning, picking and turning them.*

The dice flew toward him again, and one spun for a few seconds before settling down.

"Three, craps, loser on the pass line, pay don't-pass, pay the field," repeated the stickman, who looked as tired as the players and in far worse shape, his paunch extending over the layout, even though he was a fairly young man.

Two hundred dollars of his money had just gone down the drain with this lousy shooter, who seemed to be able to throw nothing but craps, and Thornton wondered whether he should bet wrong, bet don't-pass. The shooter was a sure loser, but you never could tell when that big roll came, when the shooter held the hot hand, and he remembered times before, missing that big roll, while he waited with his lousy don't-pass bet, waited a full half hour while all that came up on the dice were numbers.

So he put another $200 on the pass line, and watched the dice fly across the table to him.

"Twelve, craps, pays double on the field," said the

stickman, as a universal moan rose from the players at the table. The 12 was a loser on the pass line, and already Thornton had given back half of the money he had won at blackjack.

Time to double it, to make it all back. He put four black checks on the pass line. *Now, you stupid Beady-Eyes,* he said silently, *give me that seven.*

"Got a light?" the woman asked him.

"What?"

"Got a light?"

"Oh, yes. Wait." He found some matches in his jacket pocket and lit her cigarette.

"Thanks," she said. "I saw you playing twenty-one. How'd you do?"

"Won a few bucks. How about you?"

"Losing. I nearly always lose. I don't even know why I play craps."

"You live here in Vegas?"

"Yes, how about yourself?"

"I'm from Chicago."

"On a junket?"

"No, I'm a lone wolf."

The dice came bounding down the table.

"Seven, winner on the pass line," the stickman yelled, and Thornton decided against making another bet. He had had enough of Beady-Eyes's shooting, and he was even at the table, which was more than could be said for any of the other players slumped around the rails, looking down at the layout with defeated faces.

"That makes me even," he told the woman. "Care to have a drink?"

"I want to make one more bet."

She put down two red $5 checks on the pass line.

"Here," said Thornton, placing a green check next to her bet, "we'll be partners on this bet, me and you."

She smiled at him and winked. Beady-Eyes rolled the dice, and a 4 came up. The hard 4, 2 and 2.

"Four came hard, bet it hard, make it come out. Bet the hardways, make that 4, shooter." This stickman never stopped his spiel.

Thornton placed another quarter check behind the line as an odds bet at 2 for 1. It took five more rolls, but the shooter hit the 4 the easy way, and it was a winner on the pass line. The dealer paid him $75 and Thornton left the table a winner.

"How about that drink?" he asked the woman.

"Sure."

On the way to the lounge, Thornton handed her two green checks. "Take this." he said. "You didn't think I forgot our partnership, did you?"

She smiled and winked again.

"What's your name?" he asked, as they sat down in the lounge.

"Diane. What's yours?"

It was five o'clock in the morning before Thornton returned to his hotel room. The sun was coming over the eastern mountains, and the day was already a blaze of light. *God,* he thought, *the heat is brutal here.* Every time he came to Vegas, it was the same thing, the intense light that could blind you, and the overwhelming heat.

He took off his limp jacket and hung it up. One plane ride and one evening in Vegas and it already looked like a rag. Putting it into the closet, he could still smell Diane's perfume. She had taken him back to her place after a couple of drinks in the lounge, in her silver Continental. That was traveling in style.

Her young woman's figure was so incredibly lovely, so firm and strong and slim. He didn't know what was going to happen when he got to her apartment, and all he did was fumble for her breasts, but she told him it was the wrong night for that; they could meet again.

So Thornton returned to the El Capitan, feeling horny as hell. He wished he had a woman, but it was early morning, and he hadn't slept in over twenty-four hours, and later on he had to get up and make that call to the dealer. He looked at his watch. It was five-thirty. *Why wait to call, why prolong the anxiety?*

He left the room and went down to the casino again. No sense in calling from the room. His conversation might be overheard, and that's all he needed. The casino was emptier than before, with only the rearguard players gambling, the losers trying to get even before they were washed away by the daylight.

Thornton called Teddy's number from a public phone and waited six rings before the dealer got on with a sleepy voice.

"Teddy, this is Lee Thornton."

"What?" The voice was uncomprehending.

"This is Lee Thornton."

"What time is it?"

"Five-thirty."

"Christ, man, I asked you to call at ten."

"Teddy, I'm calling now. What's the scoop?"

"Huh?"

"You wanted me to call you. What's happening?"

"Oh . . . yeah. Look, Mr. Thornton, something's come up, you know? I got a partner and he asked me to cool it this week. It's a bad time; I don't have to tell you why, do I?"

"Then our arrangement is off?"

"Yeah, afraid so. Can't help it."

"OK. Well, goodbye."

Thornton hung up the phone. Suddenly the fatigue that he had been fighting swept over him. He could feel how clammy and tired his body was. Time to go back to the room. Thornton walked slowly through the casino, not watching the action, anxious to get back and get out of his clothes—the same stinking ones he had put on in Chicago the morning before, which now seemed like a year ago.

Back in his room, Thornton thought about the dealer. Damn that Teddy, killing all his plans for this week. The last time he stayed in Vegas, Thornton remembered, he had a room at the Riviera but played all over the Strip. One night, at the El Capitan, he played at Teddy's table, playing head to head with him, the only player at the table. They started a conversation, and Teddy gave Thornton his phone number and told him to call the next day. They met at Marie Callender's, a restaurant on Sahara that specialized in home-made pies. Over strawberry pie and ice cream, they worked out a deal. Teddy would signal his hole card to Thornton for 50 percent of the profits. They practiced the signal at Teddy's apartment, and that night Thornton won over $6,000. It was his last night in Vegas, and it was his biggest win ever. Afterwards he split the money with Teddy, giving him only $2,000, and they had a fight about the division of the spoils.

Thornton swore to Teddy that the split was right and believed he had conned the dealer, but maybe, he thought, as he lay in bed, maybe that was why Teddy didn't want to work with him. Maybe he blew it, but he smiled, knowing that he had plans again to screw the dealer out of his rightful share if they played again.

That was the story of his life, grabbing what he could. He wondered why he was like that, but it was in his blood. Maybe he'd inherited it from his father, who, as a clerk in the court system, took money left and right. Whatever it was, it had put him into a bind, one that he found hard to get out of.

Right now, for example, he was playing with money borrowed from his clients, without their knowledge. He had been doing it for a few years now to support his gambling debts, but never on the current scale. This week was now-or-never week, make-or-break week. He had to win at least $20,000 to pay off everything, to get even.

If he could really make a killing this trip, really hit it big, then he could make other plans. They were all on the edge of his unconscious, and he didn't even want to think about them yet, but he knew he couldn't continue his life in Chicago, with a father-in-law who despised him and a wife he felt nothing for. If only he could have one good hour in his life, one exciting hour.

He couldn't have it in Chicago, but Vegas was something else. Yes, he thought, closing his eyes, he was embarking on an adventure this week. He could make his fantasies come to life.

Never before had he had so much money to play with, almost $60,000. He would move out of his fantasies into the real world. The money was real, even Vegas was real.

With his eyes closed, Thornton could feel fatigue numb his brain. He was going under, into that world he was most at home in, happiest in, that secret world of his dreams.

Wednesday

4

Harry Milner turned the Porsche 914, its white body glistening in the sun, into the left-turn lane on Las Vegas Boulevard South, and waited for the traffic oncoming in the opposite lane to go by before pulling into the driveway of the El Capitan Hotel and Casino. He drove slowly, so that the raised humps of asphalt painted with diagonal yellow stripes wouldn't jar the Porsche, and then parked under the canopy. He got out of the car as one of the parking-lot boys came bounding up.

"Good afternoon, Mr. Milner."

"Afternoon, Sam. Leave it in the shade, will you?"

"Right, Mr. Milner."

Milner stood near the front entrance, taking off his dark glasses and carefully putting them into his jacket pocket. He was a stocky man of medium height, with a round face dominated by gray eyes. The eyes were inquisitive and the face had a calm, intelligent aspect to it. There were no lines on his face, and only a receding hairline and flurries of gray hair in his sideburns gave away his age, which was fifty-two.

The darkness of the casino interior smothered his vision, and he had to pause for a few moments after the intense sunlight outside before he could see clearly. Only a few people were at the reservations desk, and Milner looked at his watch. It was ten after one. The New York junket should have come in by now.

Milner went over to the bell captain.

"Where's the New York junket?" he asked.

"It's delayed, Mr. Milner. Should arrive at one-thirty."

"Here or at McCarran?"

"Here."

"Let me know when it comes in."

"Will do."

Milner walked away from the desk and went into the casino area, stopping to light a cigarette and look over the place. It was moderately busy for a Wednesday afternoon— not too bad, considering that both the New York and Chicago junkets weren't in yet. There were going to be over 150 warm bodies on each plane, premium gamblers who really could make a casino hum. The place would soon be jumping with those fresh, warm bodies.

To Milner's right, as he surveyed the scene inside the casino, was a forest of slot machines, their glass and steel exteriors studded with blue, red, and yellow lights—an electric jungle that was very profitable to the El Capitan. The 470 slots generated almost a million dollars' worth of profits a year, even though the majority were just nickel machines.

Right now, most of the players were women. How the women loved the machines, Harry thought. If they took care of their husbands the same way, well . . .

He inhaled the smoke deeply and turned his attention to the blackjack pit. Of the twelve tables, six were in operation, but the others would open right up once that junket came in. Junkets. God, how his business depended on junkets. They accounted for half the gaming profits.

He walked by the pit slowly, pausing to watch the pit-boss and floormen in action and to check out the one $100 table that was open. A single player was at that table, playing two hands and betting $200 a hand. Milner watched him bust on both hands. He recognized the customer as a steady player from LA, who came in a couple of times a month at the El Capitan's expense. The guy had a $50,000 credit line at the casino. Milner wished he had a hundred more like him.

Past the blackjack pit were two roulette tables, only one of which was in use, and this one was empty. Roulette was a comparatively dead proposition at the El Capitan. On rare occasions some fools would come in with a surefire system and give the tables a real play, but it was more of a grind operation here, and now the dealer was standing motionless, his arms crossed, his face blank with boredom. He didn't even notice Milner walk by.

A short aisle separated this area from the real money-makers, the craps tables. There were six in the El Capitan, each one capable of producing close to a million dollars' worth of profits a year. What they actually *were* taking in was much less, but that was another story, thought Milner.

He peered at the tables, just to gauge the action. At craps 2, one of the boxmen looked up, caught Milner's gaze, then nodded to the stickman, who suddenly started perking up the game.

"Point is 8," yelled the stickman, "bet the hard 8, bring it out. Bet the field, come bets, bet the hardways. Let's get those bets down on the hardways. Make that 8, shooter."

The dice were thrown the length of the table. There was a pause, and from the silence, Milner, who had been a dealer at craps in his day, knew that the shooter had sevened out. His hunch was confirmed by the stickman.

"Seven, line away. New shooter coming out. How about the field, hardways? Craps 11. Who'll bet craps 11?"

Milner kept walking. A couple of people moved to craps 3, and one asked for a marker for five hundred; action would pick up there. Only three of the tables were now going, and Moe Lewis would probably open up one or two more tables when the junkets arrived. Maybe all the tables, but that was optimistic. Tomorrow night, when Mike English performed, that would be another story. The place would be crawling with warm bodies tomorrow night.

At the rear of the casino was the baccarat pit, now empty of players. It had just opened about an hour ago, and generally it caught on at night. Milner was thinking of introducing mini-baccarat to the El Capitan, but he wondered if that would end the regular baccarat game, a big money-maker. He looked over the dealers at the table, all in tuxedos, and the three women shills, all Vegas show-girl types, a little over the hill, all with coiffed hair and tight smiles. Vegas women had the tightest smiles.

Next to the baccarat pit was the cashier's cage, and next to the cage was the entrance to the executive offices. Stopping just long enough to look over the cage, Milner opened the door marked "Executives Only" and went into the corridor, at the end of which was his office, marked in gold letters, "H. Milner, President."

He went by Moe Lewis's office, the door of which was open, though Moe wasn't in his office. Moe's closed-circuit TV was on and was focused on one of the empty craps tables. It was a strange sight, that empty table on the TV screen. A surrealistic sight, thought Milner, heading for his office.

Betty Leavitt, his secretary, was waiting for him at her small desk outside his office.

"You have a couple of calls. Nothing important. And Moe Lewis wants to see you."

"Where is he? He wasn't in his office."

"In the coffee shop. You want me to page him?"

"No, when he comes back, send him in. Anything else?"

"No."

"Bring me some coffee, would you, Betty?"

"Yes, Mr. Milner."

In his office Milner went to the closet and took off his jacket, then walked to the picture window, which overlooked the grounds of the El Capitan. He could see the swimming pool and the tennis courts. There were several people lying beside the pool sunbathing and a few in the water, but no one was at the courts. You had to be crazy to play tennis at midday in July in Vegas.

He squinted into the light, then drew the drapes across the window and glanced at the clock above his desk, the hours set with dice. Right now the small hand was just past a single die, and the large hand hovered near the hard four. The junket was expected in ten minutes.

Milner sat down and lit another cigarette, then signed some letters. Moe Lewis came into the office a moment later, followed by Betty with a pot of coffee. Milner waited for her to leave, then poured himself a cup. Moe Lewis had a bad stomach and never drank coffee.

"So, what's happening, Moe?" he asked the casino manager.

"Harry, I want to speak to you."

"What about?"

"It's about Mike English."

"What about him?"

"He's been breaking my balls, Harry. He wants credit in the casino."

Milner dragged in a load of smoke and blew it out slowly. Moe Lewis fished out a half-dead cigar and lit it with stubby fingers. Cigar odor immediately filled the room.

"He wants credit, Harry. I told him, no credit. That's in his contract, isn't it? No credit?"

"That's right, it's in his contract. He can't get credit in

the casino. All the checks go directly to his manager in LA."

"Well, you better speak to him."

"I will. I'll take care of it," said Milner.

"He went to Chet also, but Chet told him to see me, and I told him to see you."

"I'll take care of it."

Moe Lewis puffed on his cigar and blew out more foul smoke.

"Balofsky called me this morning," Milner said. The casino manager stared at him. "Yes, he called. He has a definite buyer for the El Capitan."

"When did he tell you this?"

"This morning."

"A real buyer?"

"That's what he said. And he told them we're going to have a winning month. Mr. B needs the El Capitan to show a profit for July." The casino manager's face was inscrutable. Milner thought, *he's worried about his job in the casino if it's sold.* Moe was in his sixties now; he wasn't a spring chicken, but what the hell, it was time for him to retire. He had points in the El Capitan; he could afford to retire.

"Not this month," said Moe. "We won't have a winning month this time around."

"Maybe yes, maybe no."

"No way, Harry."

"Moe, we have English opening. He's going to draw the crowds. He'll bring them in. And we have two good junkets arriving today. We can make it."

"We'll see," said Lewis. "Mr. B keeps talking about unloading. He's been talking about that for years, Harry."

"Well, now Uncle Sam has an interest. He's putting a lot of pressure on our Mr. B."

Moe took the cigar out of his mouth and ground it out

in an ashtray on Milner's desk. "What else did he have to say?"

"The buyers have been examining the books all week long," Milner said. "And the books are showing a projected profit for this month. They're going to come here in person on Sunday."

"This Sunday?" Lewis wiped away some tobacco that was sticking to his bottom lip.

"That's right." Milner lit a cigarette. "And Tiny Shapiro and Mr. B's nephew, Leon, are coming here tomorrow. You know them, don't you?"

"Sure I know them, Harry. Tiny and I go back a long ways in this town. From the beginning."

"They're coming to make sure that everything holds together for the sale. They've also been going over the books with a fine-tooth comb."

Lewis shifted in his seat. "Listen, Harry, I already knew about Tiny coming out here. And I know who else he's bringing besides Leon." He waited for Milner to look up at his face.

"Who else?"

"Augie Panetta. He's coming out from Detroit, today or tomorrow."

Milner sat back and stared at his casino manager. "What the hell are you talking about?"

"Just what I said."

"Are you kidding me, Moe?"

"I don't kid about such things."

"How's he going to get off the plane? They'll send him right back. They won't let him set foot in Nevada."

"He can get in. We all know that."

"What's the point?"

"Hey, Harry, you know he has an interest now in this place. And you know how things are here. We're having trouble with our hold percentage. If things aren't kosher, well, Augie can straighten that out in a hurry."

Milner sipped the coffee, but it was tepid. He had lost his interest in the coffee anyway. "I don't like that," he said, "interest or no interest. He's bad news, Moe."

"But that's what I hear; he's coming in."

"Where'd you hear it?"

"Shit, Harry, where'd I hear it? I heard it, that's where."

Milner coughed. He had a bad taste in his mouth. Too many cigarettes. "You see the drop figures for yesterday?"

"Yeah, they stunk, like Monday's. We're getting hurt on blackjack on the swing shift."

"We had a lousy show," said Milner. "With English opening, things are going to turn around."

"We never should have put in the four-deck games," said Lewis. "The players like the one-deck games."

"That's not what's hurting us. The whole town is switching to four decks. It's a faster game, and a safer game. We can't get hurt by counters or cheating players."

"I don't know."

"It's the show . . . you'll see. With English, the women will swarm in, and the premium customers will follow."

The casino manager shrugged. "I better get back to the floor," he told Milner.

"OK."

After Moe Lewis left, Milner went to the small washroom in his office and splashed water on his face, combing his sparse hair carefully. He looked a little puffy in the mirror.

The phone rang. It was the front desk, telling him that the junket from New York had arrived. Milner hung up the phone but didn't have the energy to go to the floor. He sat and thought about Moe, and what Moe had told him.

Augie Panetta. The guy was a mad hatter, a stone killer.

33

There had been something in the papers a couple of years back about his involvement in some torture killings in Detroit. He was now Mr. B's partner, but why should he come to Vegas? It was no good.

He thought of Mr. B on the phone that morning, that familiar gruff voice he had heard so often. Balofsky was going to unload the El Capitan, no matter what Moe thought. And the new people were definitely coming Sunday. Well, he'd show them a good week at least. If this week was good, July would be a winning month.

A winning month. That's what he needed. That would solve all his problems. And with the new owners, he could forget about Panetta and Tiny Shapiro and Mr. B. The new owners would probably let him get his own crew in the casino.

If the owners wanted him. Well, he couldn't worry about that right now. All he could do was his job, and do it right. First things first, and first and foremost, Milner told himself, get that winning month.

5

Milner had come to Las Vegas as an accountant, at his cousin Bill's insistence. Bill had written that the town was growing by leaps and bounds and there was plenty of opportunity for a smart young man like Harry. Milner grabbed at the opportunity. It was five years after World War II, and things were tough around the country.

He went to work for Bill, who had a small accounting firm downtown on Carson. What really fascinated Milner, however, was not the figures on cold white sheets of paper but the vitality of the casino scenes. Against Bill's wishes, and to the utter dismay of his family back in Baltimore, Milner became a dealer at Binion's place downtown, the Horseshoe. He dealt craps. He was one of the best. He knew how to make a table zing. When Milner was stick-man, they had the biggest drop of any crew, and the bosses quickly took notice of him.

It was a good place to start out. Binion's operation was always one of the best, as far as Harry was concerned, and he still believed the finest crap games in operation were at the Horseshoe. Sometimes they'd get as big a game going as anywhere in Vegas, although it was downtown and was patronized by a much different crowd from that which frequented the Strip hotels.

A player was a player, and some big bettors came to those craps tables, making or leaving fortunes. And the tokes were terrific. But as much as he liked the job and the excitement, liked to call a game and be part of the action, Milner had other ambitions. He didn't want to be a dealer all his life, and when he was offered a job as a boxman at the Fremont, he accepted.

It was a tamer position, but one step up the ladder. The boxman sat and watched an entire craps table and was directly responsible to the management for its supervision. There were disadvantages, however. The biggest drawback was that he didn't share in the tips, for though the boxman made about twice the salary of the dealers, the money was in the tokes.

And when you weren't actively part of the game, handling the stick or making payoffs and bets for the players, time dragged. But Milner considered patience one of his strong points, and he stuck it out. He then got his toehold in the real Vegas gambling scene—a job at a Strip hotel.

He worked as a boxman at the Thunderbird, then as a floorman. This job got him away from the dice table itself and put him in a standing position in the pit, watching a few craps tables under the supervision of a pitboss, who ran the whole craps pit. It was another step up the ladder, and from there he became a pitboss at the Tropicana, which liked to bill itself as the "Tiffany of the Strip." In the 50s, Milner reflected, it was a real class place, competing with the DI, as the Desert Inn was called by the locals, for the high rollers.

In those days, the old-line hotels still held their own against the high-rise giants that were being built. The revolution in hotel concepts began in 1955 with the Riviera, the first tall casino in Vegas. It was an immediate, fantastic success and was followed quickly by hotels such as the Sands, Sahara, and Dunes.

Before the Riviera, all the hotels on the Strip had been patterned after the first big winner, the Flamingo, built by Bugsy Siegel. The format was a basic one. The casino faced the Strip, which was officially called Las Vegas Boulevard South. Separating the casino from the hotel rooms were interior grounds, with a swimming pool smack in the middle. The rooms were in buildings of two or three stories, which meant long corridors.

It was the easy way to build hotels in a place where there was plenty of acreage. Vegas was nothing but raw land, bleak desert that stretched in all directions to the surrounding mountains. But as the gambling increased, as the mobs poured into the city, as the high-rises drew the crowds, the older hotels slowly began to feel the pinch. High rollers didn't like to walk through open areas and long corridors to get back to their rooms when their pockets were stuffed with money. In the high-rises, they simply took an elevator up to their rooms and that was that.

To face the competition, the Desert Inn put up a high-rise next to the casino. It worked, but some of the other hotels, confronted with the enormous cost of doing this, held off—and suffered as a result, right up to today. Some of these old-line hotels, once showplaces on the Strip, were in serious financial trouble.

While working as pitboss at the Tropicana, Milner met

Karen Ross, a showgirl in the Folies Bergères. They had a fast courtship, and the marriage was over just about as quickly. She had her eyes set on Hollywood, and left Vegas as soon as she met a man who told her he'd get her a screen test. The last Milner heard from her, she was managing a massage parlor in Hawaii.

After the breakup of that marriage, Milner lived the life of the single man in Vegas—parties, women, gambling, the works. It was a high life for a while, but then he wanted more stability. So he married again, to a woman who was an executive at the Broadway Department Store.

He was forty-two at the time, and Mary Barnett was thirty-four. They had separate careers and he was glad that she wasn't involved in the casino world. But Mary had come from San Francisco to take the job at the Broadway, and she missed the city's cultural life. She wanted to see ballet, hear classical music, go to museums. There was none of that in Vegas. She began to take long trips to Los Angeles and San Francisco, supposedly on business—as an executive for a p.r. firm in town.

This week she was in Denver, again on some kind of business. But Milner could see what was happening. He had tried to get her at the number in Denver for two days now, and day or night, no one ever answered. Not that he cared that much. He and Mary had been married for close to ten years and now had little in common. He had his work and she had her travels.

He's soon think of his future, of new plans for himself, plans that didn't involve Mary, but meanwhile he was bogged down in the operation of the El Capitan. It was a twenty-five-hour job, seven days a week.

He knew that Mary would soon leave Vegas for good. He himself had thought about that some years back and had actually gone back to Baltimore for a few months, to see what life was like in the East again. He couldn't stand it. He was used to a place where he could get up at any hour and find action and excitement, where something was doing all the time. He knew now that Vegas was in his blood and this was where he'd make his life.

After working at the Tropicana, Milner had been offered the job at a smaller Strip hotel, the Golden West, as the casino manager. He took it without hesitation, even though the Golden West had the reputation as a sawdust place for grinds.

It was his big chance, heading an entire casino. And he turned the place upside down, building it into a real money-maker. He was then appointed assistant to the president, but he realized that was the end of the line at the Golden West. The president was a young man, a son of the leading stockholder, and Milner could never get that job.

At that time the El Capitan was having its troubles. The government had stepped in and uncovered a huge skimming operation, in which money was taken from the tables before it ever got to the counting room for tax purposes. Indictments were handed down left and right. Since it opened, the El Capitan had been run by three men, all from Detroit, all part of what the papers called the "Grosse Point Gang." The three were Sol Balofsky, John Hunt, and Max Greenberg. Greenberg got a heart attack the day he appeared in court for the first time, and two weeks later he was dead. Hunt pleaded no contest, and wound up in federal prison. Only Balofsky escaped, having gotten the indictments against himself quashed. He escaped because his home base had always been Detroit, while Hunt and Greenberg were always in Vegas, at the casino.

With Greenberg and Hunt out of the picture, Balofsky put in a quick call to Milner and offered him the presidency of the El Capitan. It was the golden opportunity he had been waiting for, but he couldn't get all he wanted.

Balofsky told him there was no chance for Milner to get points in the casino until the government cleared up the matter of taxes and other litigation was put out of the way.

The heir to Greenberg and Hunt's share of the hotel was a man named James Erickson, who lived in Miami Beach and never came to Vegas. But everyone knew he was a front man, and somehow, by a process that Milner could only guess at, Augie Panetta became a full partner of Balofsky. Since Panetta was in the black book of the Gaming Commission, he was *persona non grata* in Vegas and never stepped into the state. But Milner knew he was a force to contend with, especially if Moe Lewis's information was correct, and he was in town.

Points in a casino meant an ownership interest, which was usually given to key executives in Vegas hotels. But Milner was content to have the presidency, because he knew Balofsky was selling out, and he could then negotiate with the new owners.

What Milner inherited when he took over the hotel was a mess. He found himself knee-deep in incompetence and neglect. The absentee ownership and the government's harassment had taken their toll. Milner brought in two of his own men: Chet Gardner as credit manager and Tom Durham as publicity director. Under Milner's direction, they revamped the credit and junket structure and the entertainment policy. The kitchen was also improved, and the casino was upgraded. With each improvement, business picked up. From a hotel deep in the red, it was now moving toward stability, toward that all-important winning month. It had taken Milner almost a year to accomplish this, but profits were just around the corner.

What he couldn't control were the old-timers—men like Moe Lewis, who had been casino manager for twelve years —and his staff of pitbosses and floormen. Mr. B was loyal to them all, and there was only so much Milner could do in the casino. That would change, he knew, with the new owners. He'd show them what he had done, what he could do. Until he had that winning month, he wouldn't rest.

The clock's hands were both on two, snake eyes on the dice, and there was work to be done, always work to be done. Milner put on his jacket, and went out on the floor to inspect the junketeers pouring into the casino.

6

When Steinberg entered Diane's apartment, she was busy in the kitchen with pots and dishes. He put the bottle of wine he had brought in her refrigerator and gave her a quick hug and kiss. "Can I give you a hand?"

"No, not really. Why don't you open the wine now? I wouldn't mind some."

Steinberg found a corkscrew in one of the drawers near the sink. He poured out two glasses of wine.

She lifted her glass. "You want to make a toast?" she asked.

"You make it."

"To joy. That's my name—Diane Joy Kimberly. Did you know that?"

"No."

"I guess my mother gave it to me, thinking it would stick to me . . . you know, like a symbol."

He didn't ask whether it had or not. Taking his wineglass, Steinberg raised it to her, took a sip, and went into the living room. He seated himself on the sofa, and looked down at the small pyramid of marijuana on the coffee table.

"How was your day?" Diane asked from the kitchen.

"I did a little playing at the Dunes."

"You win?"

"Not much. Sixty bucks. Playing at a $5 table."

He closed his eyes and relaxed while she worked in the kitchen. A few minutes later she called him in. The table was set and the food was on it; broiled salmon, a salad, and steamed broccoli.

"That all looks nice," said Steinberg. "I haven't had a home-cooked meal in a long time."

"The salmon's courtesy of some dude from Portland. I made a couple of hundred bucks off him and three salmon."

"You freeze the others?"

"No, I gave them to Cindy and to another girl I know. It would have been a shame to freeze them. I think the guy carried the salmon on his lap all the way to Vegas."

Steinberg began to eat.

"I don't have any bread in the house. You don't mind, do you, Don?"

"No, I never eat bread myself."

"Is that how you stay so thin?"

"No. Aggravation at the tables."

"How come they never bar you at the Dunes? You're always winning there."

"Because I disguise my playing. They don't know I'm a counter. I was at this table today with a real card counter, beard and all. He watched every card like a hawk; you could see the wheels clicking in his head. He raised his bets from one to ten units, betting $5 chips. In a couple of minutes, a floorman was hanging around the table; next they were shuffling up after every hand. That's when I left. I figured, sixty bucks, that's a day's pay."

"Not in this town."

"Well, Diane, I can't live in the high style you do."

She looked at him to see if he was serious, then she smiled. "I have to keep up a good appearance."

"No lie." He poured out some more wine. It was a good dry Moselle. "You know, I can't remember the last time

I ate fresh fish," he told her. "That's one of the things I really miss about the East. About New England. The fresh fish."

"We didn't have it in Kansas. I don't think about it so much."

"I do. And the seasons. You ever miss the seasons? You know, snow in the winter?"

She shrugged. "I try not to think about it too much. I guess I just close off a part of my mind." Diane got up and brought back some more salmon, putting it on Don's plate. He offered to split it with her, but she shook her head.

After dinner, they went into the living room and drank the rest of the wine. Diane rolled a couple of joints. They sat on the couch, passing one back and forth.

"So you were married," said Diane. "I didn't know you were married."

"I'm not married."

"I mean, that you were married."

"I told you about that the first time I met you, over at the Dunes."

"Well, I was a little stoned. You have to tell me things twice and three times sometimes, because when I'm stoned I don't remember them."

Steinberg passed the joint to her, letting the blue smoke trickle out of his mouth.

"What happened with your marriage?" Diane asked.

Steinberg didn't answer.

"You don't want to talk about it?"

"I don't know," he said.

"I'll talk about my marriage instead. You want to hear about mine?"

"If you want to talk about it."

"There's nothing much to say. He was a big football

star and I was a cheerleader. Can you picture me as a cheerleader, in those chickie cute skirts . . . rah, rah, rah?"

"I can't."

"It's a mind-boggler. Really. But I was a cheerleader, and there was Lance, all Big Eight halfback. I really knew about football in those days. So, we got married. I wouldn't let him screw me till we got married, can you believe that?"

Steinberg said nothing, staring at the far wall.

"That's the truth, but it was a mistake. I wouldn't make the same mistake today. If I had screwed him first, I never would have married him. It was no good, none of it." She dragged in deeply, held the smoke a long time, then blew it out in one rush. "He got me pregnant and then went to training camp at Denver to try and make the pros. He didn't cut the mustard at Denver and then he went to Houston and when he couldn't make the Oilers, he tried for some minor-league team in San Antonio. When he heard I was pregnant, he wrote and told me he had a lot of thinking to do."

She let the last wisps of smoke trail out of her mouth. "I guess he did a lot of thinking because I never saw him again. He got thrown off the team for fighting or getting drunk or something—it must have been a big ego thing for him . . . And the next thing I knew some lawyer was writing to me telling me his client wanted a divorce and would pay half of it. That was Lance's way of doing things."

Diane looked at the joint. "This is strong," she said. "I get it from my LA connection." She passed the joint to Steinberg. "How long were you married?" she asked.

"How long? Three years."

"It didn't work out?"

"It worked out all right."

"No shit." She sat up straight and looked over at him. She could see Don's eyes looking into the distance, a distance not bounded by the walls of the room.

"You still in love with her?" she asked.

"There's nothing to be in love with."

Steinberg's eyes looked clouded to her; his whole face had darkened. She put a hand on his arm and rubbed it. "Is everything OK, Don? Did I say the wrong thing?"

"No, it's nothing. It's all right."

"You don't have to talk about it if you don't want to. I'm just stupid asking all these questions."

She got up and put a record on the stereo, letting the music drown out her thoughts as the Rolling Stones came on, Mick Jagger singing, "I Can't Get No Satisfaction."

"I have more wine," said Diane. "You want some more?"

"OK." Steinberg got up and went into the kitchen for the wine. He came back and poured two more glassfuls. She watched his every move. He seemed so changed to her, so . . . dark. She kept thinking of that word. His whole demeanor had changed.

Diane lit another joint. Together, the alcohol and grass made her feel warm, reassured.

Steinberg still sat silently. Then he turned to her and smiled. "Don't mind me." he said. "It must be the pot."

"No, I understand, baby. That's all right."

"That's good. I hope you understand. It's just hard to talk about, you know?"

"Sure. You don't have to talk about it."

He stood up and paced around the room. She watched him. He was about six feet tall, and lean, with broad shoulders. For a moment, she could picture him on the campus in Lawrence, Kansas, getting ready for a football game. He looked like a wide receiver.

He sat down again, this time in a chair across from her. Between them, on the coffee table, was an ornate set of

44

chessmen. He moved a pawn. "You play chess?" he asked.

"No. Some guy gave me the set and said he was going to teach me, but I never heard from him again."

"It's a good game. Once in a while I do chess problems by myself."

"What do you mean?"

"Well, you set up a problem; mate in two or three. If you knew the game, it would be easier to explain."

"Do you want to teach me sometime?"

"Sure. Sometime." He took the joint from her and dragged in the smoke, letting it fall deep down, till his lungs burned. Then he released it, feeling his head spin. *Diane was right,* he thought, *it was strong shit.*

They sat silently for a while, killing the second bottle of wine, saying nothing, letting the music pour over them.

Steinberg now felt he could hear all the instruments in the band individually, could hear all the nuances of the music. He finished the rest of the wine.

"You doing anything tonight?" Diane asked.

"No."

"You want to go out to a show or something?"

"Not particularly. But if you want to . . ."

"No, I was just asking. Cindy might be here later, but I'll tell her I'm busy."

Steinberg stretched his legs, listening to the end of a song, the end of a record, the distinct sound of the record changer lifting, a new record falling. He could hear its long fall. He closed his eyes, but his head spun too much. He opened them again. Diane was sitting with her eyes glazed, lost in thought.

She shook her head. "Don, what are you going to do?"

"Tonight?"

"Yes."

"I don't know. Go back . . ."

"Back where?"

"To my place."

"Did I make you mad . . . you know, with my questions?"

"No, it just got me thinking."

Diane closed her eyes. She could feel how tense their conversation was. What had happened? She felt so uneasy, felt that she wanted to get away herself, get on the Strip, find some action, do something . . . She knew the evening was shot with Don, was ending badly.

Thursday

7

The telephone ringing in his bedroom awakened Harry Milner. He scowled, opened his eyes, and picked up the phone. It was Tom Durham, the publicity director, calling from the El Capitan.

"Harry, we've got a problem here," said Durham.

"What's the problem?"

"Sorry to bother you, Harry, but I've got Mike English in my office. I guess I'm the last guy he came to see. Moe and Chet aren't in, and Mike is screaming bloody murder. Hold on, I'll put him on."

"Hey, Harry," began Mike English. The voice that was familiar to millions of his fans sounded a little harsh to Milner. "Hey, Harry, what is this? I go to the tables this morning and they tell me I have no credit. What is this?"

Milner was sitting up in his bed, the sheets in disarray. He groped for a cigarette and lit one, awkwardly cradling the phone between his shoulder and head.

"What was that you said?" he asked English.

"I said, Jesus, must I go through this whole shtick with you again, Harry . . . I said, I have no credit at the hotel, at the tables. Why don't I have any credit?"

"Why?" Milner couldn't seem to think straight. He took a long drag on his cigarette, feeling his head spin from the smoke. "Why?" He shifted his weight and stood up, walking with the phone, the long extension cord trailing behind him in the gold and blue decorated bedroom. "Why?" he repeated for the third time. "I'll tell you why, Mike. Because it's in your contract, that's why."

"Hey, man, what are you telling me?" came the singer's insistent voice. "What is this, a put-on? A joke, Harry?"

"No joke. It's in your contract."

"Well, man, I'm not going to hang around Vegas . . . I'm not going to hang around and not get a play at the tables. Shit, man, no way. And tell your boy here, who suggested I take a swim instead, tell him he'll wind up in the fucking pool if he keeps this up. I'll dump the fucker myself."

"All right, now take it easy, Mike. I'll be right over."

"Right over isn't fast enough," the entertainer shot back. "Right now is what is important. I've been rehearsing half the night, and I come down nice and early, and there's no way I can play. Hey, man, this is an impossible situation. I won't stand for it. No way." And he slammed down the phone.

By this time Milner was awake, trying, underneath the anxiety he felt about Mike's anger, to think of a dream he had the night before, in which his former wife was humiliating him. He dismissed the dream and made his way to the bathroom. He took off his pajama top and started washing his face, preparing to shave, when the phone rang again.

It was Mike English.

"Hey, man, I'm coming over to see you right now."

"Give me fifteen minutes, will you, Mike? Jesus, Mike, you wake me up and all . . . just give me fifteen minutes, all right?" He was surprised at his own conciliatory tone, but he realized that if Mike English pulled a tantrum and disappeared, there went this week and this month, and maybe his job. Shit, the fucking singer had him over a barrel.

"All right. In fifteen minutes," said English.

"Put Tom on the phone, would you?"

His publicity man got on.

"Tom, why didn't you get ahold of Vincente?"

"He already spoke to Vincente."

"I see." Vincente was the entertainment director. "All right, listen carefully. Tom, go to my office and take out the English file. You'll find it in the cabinet on the far wall, the brown cabinet. It'll be in the top or second drawer. Betty will let you in."

"OK."

"And after you find it, bring it right over. Come straight here. Right now."

"Got you."

"Does Mike want to speak to me?"

"He's already out the door."

"OK, remember, the brown cabinet."

After hanging up, Milner finished shaving, looking at the lines under his eyes. He needed a vacation, he told himself, one year on the job and he needed two years' vacation. *Where the fuck is Balofsky while all this is going on? That bastard, barking his orders out of his mansion in Detroit. Let him come to Vegas and get his own feet wet. Let him deal with guys like Mike English.*

Milner smiled at the thought that if these were the old days in Vegas, Mike English would be tiptoeing around. Imagine him talking that way to Balofsky . . . or Panetta. "I want it now, right now, this minute . . ." Shit, they'd find Mike English disappearing off a boat somewhere, or they'd find his left tonsil in Tonapah and his right one in Searchlight.

With this in mind, he finished his shaving, took a warm shower, and toweled himself off. By the time he was

dressed Frederica, the maid, had come in, and had coffee
ready for him in the dinette.

"Morning, Mr. Milner," she said, smiling as usual, always happy. It amazed Milner to see her this way. He
knew she had five kids to support and barely struggled
through each month, while he dealt in millions at the
hotel. Something was wrong somewhere.

Mike English was the first to arrive. He was a short man,
much shorter than his TV or movie appearances would
suggest. The mass of curly black hair on his head gave him
added height, and he was trim, in his custom-made denim
suit and beige shirt with eight-inch collar points hanging
over the lapels. He wore pink sunglasses, which he removed
and stacked in his hair.

"Harry, baby," said Mike, embracing him, as if twenty
minutes before his voice had not been filled with threats
and venom.

"Mike, Mike," said Milner, returning the empty, show-
biz gesture. "Sit down, sit down," he told the entertainer.
"Frederica, how about some coffee for our guest here? You
know Mike English, Frederica?"

The singer gave the maid a big smile, his trademark, the
smile half shy and glistening at the same time. Mike sat
down heavily into one of the white wrought-iron chairs at
the glass-topped dinette table. Frederica gave him a cup of
coffee and put toast out on a plate, heavily buttered.

"Want some eggs?" Milner asked.

"No, coffee's fine."

Milner chewed on a piece of toast, while English drank
his coffee black.

"So," asked the entertainer, "what's this bullshit, Harry,
about contracts? What are you telling me—I signed a contract that I can't play the tables?"

"You can play all you want, but you don't get credit at
the El Capitan."

"Hey, man, what do you mean, no credit? Let me see that contract."

"Tom is bringing it over, Mike. Mike, relax. Look, Mike, I don't care if you play at the tables day and night. I don't care if you lose a million at the tables. That's my business. That's what the El Capitan is there for, for players. But you have a contract . . ."

"Hey, Harry . . ."

"Mike, let me finish . . . let me finish, OK? I didn't insist on that clause. I couldn't care less. It was your manager, Arnold Goldstein. He's the one. I remember the deal. He said no credit whatsoever, and you agreed."

"Hey, hey, Harry, I never agreed. You sitting and telling me you heard me say I agreed? You telling me that?"

"I didn't hear you, no. But you signed it. You signed it in LA or wherever. We have the contract. What do you want me to do, break it? How can I break your contract?"

The singer reflected on this as the doorbell rang. Tom Durham came in with the file.

"Here," said Milner, after Tom left, as he scanned the contract. "Here it is. Read it for yourself."

"You read it to me."

"All right. It says here, wait a minute . . ." He put on his reading glasses. "It says here, '. . . that the said artist shall not be given any credit at any of the gaming tables by the said employer hotel during his employment at said hotel, and in the event such credit is given, the parties agree that it shall not be the duty of said artist, his manager, agent, or representatives to honor such credit.' "

"It goes on further," said Milner. "Do you want to hear the rest of it?"

"No."

"It's clear," said Milner. "Now what do you want me to do?"

Mike English sat back in his chair and eyed the president of the El Capitan Hotel and Casino. He took a deep breath, his lips thin, he face pink, mottled by freckles.

"If I can't play, I'm not going on tonight."

"Look, Mike, the last time you were in Vegas was six, seven years ago, right?"

"Six years ago."

"Not at my hotel, right?"

"Right. And I could play all I wanted."

"What happened, Mike?" asked Milner in a soft voice, but from the reaction he quickly knew he had made a bad mistake asking that question.

"What happened, you ask? What the fuck are you asking me? What else do you want to know? Shit, man, don't pull that on me, also. Everyone and his brother asks me, hey, Mike, what happened in Vegas? What happened with Dolores and that English guy? What happened with Carol? What happened with Joan? What happened, what happened? And you're asking me, now, what happened? I'll tell you something, Harry . . ."

He paused, out of breath, then resumed. "I'll tell you . . . . this is another day and another year. I had my troubles, but this is today. Today is today, right?" He cleared his throat and continued. "I don't want to explain anything to you, or to anyone. I won't explain things to my own mother. All I'm asking you—I'm telling you—is that I want to play. I don't give a shit about papers, and contracts, and that bullshit. I've had lawyers put me through the wringer, wring me out, fuck me over, and rip me off. Screw the lawyers and their papers. I'm telling you . . ."

He stood up, his face very pink, and paced around the room. "I'm telling you, Harry, and I'm putting it simply. Either I play, either you work something out this morning, or I pack my bags and take off, and the El Capitan can take its twenty-five G's a week and shove it. It's peanuts, and you can shove it."

Milner stared at the entertainer, then told Frederica to bring more coffee. "There's a contract here," he said.

Mike English exploded again. "Listen, Harry, don't tell me about papers."

"All right, all right. I'll tell you what. I'll call your manager. If he agrees . . ."

"If he agrees? What about me? Who the fuck is Arnold Goldstein? What about me?"

"Mike. Mike, I can't just give you credit. If you lose and don't pay, I have to answer to my bosses. I have bosses over me. I just can't do it on my own. But we can do it right. I'll call up Arnold and we'll speak to him. You speak to him."

English was still pacing around the room. Milner expected him to bolt out the door and disappear forever. But the singer sat down and had more coffee. He finished a second cup before he spoke again.

"Get me a phone, Harry."

Milner took a deep breath. He wasn't going to be Mike's servant. There were limits. "The phone's in the living room. We'll call from there." He got up and went into the living room, with Mike following.

The singer took out a little black book from his pocket and leafed through the pages. He took the phone from Harry and dialed a number, listened, grimaced, and slammed the receiver down. "It's his answering service in the office. Shit." He dialed another number, and it was answered by a woman. "Fay, how's it going? What's happening? . . . This is Mike, yeah. Let me speak to Arnold . . . Yeah, yeah."

The hotel president, sitting on the sofa, rubbed his hands against his trouser sides. He could feel how sweaty they were. This bastard was causing this, this little bastard, this has-been. Give him a break, he thought, and he does this. Milner knew he'd learn his lesson one day, but he didn't quite know what the lesson was, when you needed a singer to open that night, when you had an ad campaign centered around him, when you were sold out for the next three nights, and the bastard was an inch away from flying off to nowhere.

English was now speaking to his manager. "Yeah, Arnold baby, yeah, calling from Lost Wages . . . Yeah . . . Yeah. Arnold, I'm over here with Harry . . . Harry Milner, at his home . . . Yeah. Arnold, there's something here about a contract—it says I can't get credit in the casino . . . Yeah." He listened intently, then handed the phone to Milner.

"Hello," said Harry.

"Harry, how are you? Good speaking to you again, Harry." came the rasping voice of the manager. "What's with my boy? What's this talk about credit?"

"He wants to play."

"Christ, no. We ironed that out months ago. Harry, whose idea is this?"

"Arnold, it's not mine, if that's what you want to know. It's his all the way."

"What do you think?"

"What do I think? All I know is that Mr. Mike English says he's going to take the next flight to somewhere if he doesn't get it."

"Put him on, would you?"

English got on, smiling. The smile irritated Milner. He lit another cigarette and listened to English arguing. Then he was handed the phone again.

"Give him fifteen big ones for the two weeks," said Arnold.

"Fifteen for the two weeks? Hold on." He turned to

the singer. "Did you hear that, Mike? Fifteen for two weeks. Is that OK?"

"Beautiful," said English, "just beautiful."

"Fine, that's what he'll get," Milner told the manager. "Now, Arnold, send me something in writing to that effect."

"It'll go right out, Harry."

"In the meantime, I'm going to have Mike sign the change right here on my contract. But I want that note from you."

"Harry, you have my word on it."

"Fair enough."

"Could I say something to Mike?"

"Sure." Mike got on the phone again. He talked to Arnold for another minute, then hung up.

"Well, happy now?" Milner asked the singer.

"I'm going to take the El Capitan," said Mike. "I'm going to empty those trays, Harry."

Milner got the contract and turned to the clause. "Just sign here," he told English. "I'm making the change on this contract." Milner crossed out the no-credit clause and wrote in "$15,000 credit at the gaming tables for the two weeks," and had Mike sign.

"Well, that's it," said Mike. "Let me call a cab. I want to get to that casino."

"I'll give you a ride."

"No, don't trouble yourself. I'll just call a cab."

After English left, Milner went into the dinette and had another cup of coffee. He ate a hot sweet roll with this coffee and listened to Frederica humming as she worked in the kitchen. He envied her tranquillity. Every time he opened his eyes, there were problems.

Mike English, that stupid bastard. Mike had been destroyed, utterly and finally destroyed at the tables six years before. He'd gone into debt in the six figures, and it was known not only in Vegas but throughout the entertainment world. It had killed his career; no one would touch him with a ten-foot pole. And it had killed his marriage to Dolores Bridget. And now, struggling to get back on top, he couldn't stay away from the tables. Sickness.

It was sick, all so sick. There was Frederica, happy in the kitchen, while the rest of Vegas sweated over their bills, and the craps tables burned out a million souls . . . There was something sick about this whole thing, and he knew it was best not to think about it too much.

8

When Mike English got to the El Capitan it was just after ten o'clock in the morning, and his favorite game, baccarat, didn't open until noon. He had worked out a system for baccarat during the last few years, all inactive years as far as gambling was concerned—years in which he went into bankruptcy, settled his tax problem with Uncle Sam, got divorced by Dolores Bridget, and got divorced again after a highly publicized year-long marriage to an eighteen-year-old. All in all, years of utter shit.

Now, for the first time in all those years, he had credit at a casino, action ready for him. But it wasn't quite like the old days, when he had six songs on the charts at once, when he had four number-one albums in a row, when he collected a dozen platinum and gold records. No, it wasn't like those days when he could go for fifty grand a night and not even feel it.

These were different times, English reflected as he walked slowly through the casino, avoiding the stares of the tourists. Only the craps players didn't pay attention. Shit, he thought, if an octopus fought a gorilla on the layout, they'd still be pressing up their bets and throwing quarter checks on the hardways.

Yes, he knew best that these weren't the same days after a gig—when he was bone tired, when his legs trembled and cramped with the forty-one years they carried, when he looked in the mirror in the morning and the face looked old and haggard, when the makeup wasn't there hiding the wrinkles. I'm getting fucking old, he told himself nearly every morning, and though he kept his hair dyed a dark brown and the hairdresser made the curls and the color, his chest hairs were almost completely gray and he was getting a little hard of hearing in the left ear.

Oh for twenty years ago, when the young women ran after him, when they screamed and shook when he went on stage, when he laid every beautiful woman he wanted to, when his wife was Carol Durst, a big star herself, and when he met Dolores Bridget.

Yes, he thought, edging past the blackjack pit, on the way to an almost empty craps table, *oh yes,* when he first saw Dolores Bridget undressing in his bedroom, when he saw those milky breasts, those blue veins on her breasts, so light and delicate, and her dark pubic hair, black and bushy, *oh, yes.*

Shit, if he didn't want to go and jerk off right now, he'd better get Dolores out of his mind. That was where she was at her best, in his mind; her body and face twelve years ago, when they both were married to other people and when every meeting was intrigue and wild excitement. And now Dolores was fat and over the hill, no longer worth anything to anybody except for her name, which kept her a star. Her face and figure were gone, but after all, she was Dolores Bridget. No one would ever take that name away from her, and what that name had represented, the most glamorous and beautiful woman in the world.

And she belonged to me, soul and mind and body, he thought, standing at the craps table, and raising his right hand, showing five fingers.

"Five thousand, Mike?" the dealer asked, grinning, happy to have him at the table. That meant the table would fill right up, and with big bettors, premium players, not nickel-and-dime grinds. And with the celebrity leading the way, the tokes would flow. Everyone would want to show Mike English that he was a high roller too.

The game filled immediately, even before the casino checks were handed to the singer. The pitboss himself, Al Beatty, came over with the marker, and English signed with a flourish. The dice had been held by a young kid who had just sevened out, and they moved around the table, right to Mike English.

He looked over the selection of dice offered to him, ten in all, and he picked two showing aces on the cubes. Then he glanced at his rails, which were filled with black checks. It wasn't much, and it wasn't what he used to start with, but it was something to play around with. He held the dice in his right hand and decided to bet $500 on the pass line.

Only fifty checks. A small bad run and it could all go, but he didn't feel unlucky. Maybe this was going to be his morning. The table was now packed with players, ogling the singer and betting heavily on the pass line. No one was betting don't-pass against Mike English.

Mike took the dice, shook them softly and flung them across the table. He watched their progress, bouncing off the far walls, and an 8 came up.

"Eight came easy, bet it hard. Hardway 8, Mike?" the stickman asked.

"Sure, one and one." He threw out a black check and watched the stickman hold it.

"Change color," he told the stickman, "and put two quarter checks on that hard 8."

One and one meant one bet for the player and one for the dealers, and his example was followed by a shower of

58

red and green checks thrown toward the stickman, all on that hard 8, which paid 10 for 1.

"Come on, hard 8," he yelled, rolling the dice again. In his excitement he forgot to make a back-line odds bet or a come bet. The dice came up snake eyes.

"Two, craps, pays double on field," yelled the stickman. "Mike, make that hard 8."

"I got the craps out of my system," he told the stickman, picking up the dice again.

"Hey, Mike," yelled a player, "do it for us, Mike. For us."

"It's hard enough doing it for myself these days," Mike answered, grinning.

The table laughed it up. Mike felt good, felt relaxed, in his element. Action!

The singer put $500 behind the line at odds of 6 for 5 on the 8, and threw out $600 in checks to the dealer.

"On the 6."

"Right, Mike." The $600 rested on the place number 6 on the layout. If it came up before the 7, the payoff was 7 for 6.

"How about the hard 6, Mike?" asked the stickman.

"Why not?" He threw out the two quarter checks. "One and one."

He shook the dice and hurled them against the other side of the table.

"Five, no field," said the stickman, playing with the dice with his stick, turning and returning the dice while payoffs were being made on the place number 5.

"Give me those dice," said English. He shook them fiercely this time, tightened his lips, and hurled them against the far wall of the table.

"Nine, center field," said the stickman, as a whoop went up from one bettor who had put $500 on the 9. He got back $700 in profits for the last roll.

"Where's that 8?" asked Mike, shaking the dice again. "Even numbers," he yelled after the dice, as they bounced around the layout, caroming off the sides of the cushions.

"Six the hard way," yelled the stickman, excited by the results of the roll. It meant $200 in tokes for the dealers at the table, and the $25 bet still remained, still working.

"Give that gentleman $200," the stickman said to the dealer on his left, pointing the stick at Mike. "And thank you very much, Mike. We sure do appreciate it."

English smiled and winked at the dealer. He had collected not only the $200 for the hardway, but an additional $700 for getting that 6. Maybe this was going to be his morning after all.

"Even numbers," he yelled after the dice as they splattered against the end cushion.

"Three, craps," said the stickman, "loser on the come bet." A dealer wiped off a couple of green checks that had been bet on the come box.

"Even numbers," yelled Mike, getting the dice off this time with a flick of the wrist.

"Eight the hard way," screamed the dealer, and the table screamed after him. "Pay the line, winning line bet," the stickman instructed. Everyone was happy and whooping it up. The dealers made another $200 in tokes from the roll, and the bets were still there, on the hardways.

Mike watched with pleasure as he got paid off, $500 for the line bet and $600 for the odds bet. He pushed the black checks into the rails. He had already collected $2,000, and the roll was getting warmed up.

His $500 bet remained on the pass line. Mike waited impatiently for the dice to return to him, but there were a lot of payoffs. He smiled as he watched the boxmen study the payoffs being made. They looked a little worried. Well, he'd really scare them now.

Hearing the noise from the table, people were rushing to craps 4 and were standing three and four deep around it, trying to get in on the hot table. And people jumped up and down, trying to get a better look at the shooter.

Finally English had those two cubes in his hand. He shook them, then threw them with the same flick of the wrist that had given him that hard 8 the roll before.

"Come on, 7," he called after them, but a hard 4 came up, 2 and 2.

"Four the hard way," the stickman said. "Mike, how about the hard 4? Make it come out, Mike."

Mike threw a black check to the stickman. "Hard 4 and hard 10, one and one on each. Now I have the hardways all covered, don't I?"

"All the hardways," confirmed the dealer.

Now he was ready. But not yet. This was the time to make some more bets. He bet $600 on the 8, and put $500 behind the line on the 4, at odds of 2 for 1.

He picked up the dice. "Even numbers," he yelled, "even numbers."

"Nine, a center field," said the stickman, but it did Mike no good. He watched in dismay as several big bettors got $700 for that roll.

"Give me those dice." He got them back and flung them hard as he could. One bounced off the far wall and landed right in the center of the layout, on the hardways box.

"Six," said the stickman, "came easy." The hardway 6 bets were removed as the dice showed 2, 4. "Thanks anyway," the stickman told Mike.

"Just give me those dice," said Mike. He had collected $700 for making that 6. Now he needed numbers, even numbers.

"Even numbers," he screamed again.

It was an 11 on the next roll. "Yo-leven," said the stickman, "a winner on the come line, winner on the field."

But none of the tough players at the table had bet either one on that roll.

Mike felt hot now. The numbers would come out, all of them. Right now. He took ten black checks, $1,000 worth, and dropped them on the table. "Nine and 5," he told the dealer, "$500 on each."

Every number but the 10 was covered. He might as well get all those numbers down. He dropped another $500 on the layout.

"Buy the 10."

"That's a quarter more," the dealer said.

"All right. Change color." He dropped another black check down and got back three green quarter checks.

"Numbers." The dice hit the far cushion and bounded to the center of the layout.

"Five," the stickman said, and the players at the table went wild. With this roll turning hot, everyone had bets down on the place numbers.

Mike was given $700 for the roll, and he threw back $500. "Press up that 5," he told the dealer.

The next roll was a 9, and he pressed that up also. Now he had $1,000 on the 9 and the same amount on the 5, plus all his other bets. A few more numbers right now and he'd empty the fucking trays.

Waiting for the dice, he studied the boxmen. How he loved to make them sweat. How they had tormented him years ago, when he went down the drain, smiling secretly as he couldn't buy a winning bet. Now they'd sweat. It was their turn.

"Numbers," he yelled after the dice.

"Yo-leven," cried the stickman, but no one collected on that roll.

The next roll was an 8, the easy way. He collected another $700.

And now, he felt, he was ready for the big push. He was poised to take it all. A few more numbers. He'd press the next one up, and then he'd bring them to their knees.

He shook the dice and flung them hard against the far corner of the table, where they were lost among the stacks of checks put on the place numbers. The dealer at that end carefully pulled the dice out. "Seven, line away," said the stickman, and suddenly, Mike's roll was at an end.

"Mother . . ." he yelled, but the crowd didn't laugh with the singer as the checks were quickly removed from the layout. English took all his checks from the rails and dropped them on the table. "Credit that marker," he told the dealer. The boxman nodded to the singer.

English didn't wait for them to add it up. He didn't even know if he came out winning or losing. What was lost was the excitement of the roll, a hot roll that died on him. He walked away from the table, and a middle-aged woman asked for his autograph. He signed quickly and gave back her ballpoint pen. He left the casino and headed across the lawn, past the swimming pool, toward his suite of rooms. He felt down. Damn, if only those numbers had come through for him. He was so close to killing that table, so close.

He had to do something now. He'd have to come down or go up, he didn't know which. Maybe snort some coke, that might do it. Or call Rhonda.

That's what he'd do. He'd call her when he got back to his room. She could fly out this afternoon, so they could celebrate his opening together.

Rhonda was different from the others. She was majoring in film at UCLA, and she was pure and beautiful and intelligent. He'd already had Arnold show her around, make some contacts for her. She was someone he could talk to, someone he could trust. He was sure of her. She wouldn't be screwing for every guy who fed her a line in Magicland. No way.

He'd call her when he got back to his suite. He could now imagine her soft voice, her face, her body. That's what he needed right now. Oh, yes.

The singer hurried to his room.

9

"Want some coffee or something?" Diane asked Lee Thornton, as he sat down in the living room of her apartment and stretched his legs under the coffee table. She'd been asleep when Thornton had rung her doorbell, and she was now only barely awake.

"No, not right now. But you go ahead and have some."

She was in the kitchen, putting a spoonful of Taster's Choice into a cup she had just rinsed out. She added boiling water and stirred it all up, then added sugar and milk, and brought the cup back into the living room. "Sure I can't give you something, some wine or anything?"

"No, I just ate, thank you."

Diane was wearing a bathrobe, and she carefully sat down, covering her legs with the folds of the robe. They were both sitting on the couch. Diane shifted her position so she could look at Thornton. "You been playing?" she asked.

"Yes. That's what this town's about, isn't it?"

"I guess so."

"If they didn't have gambling in Vegas, who would come here?"

"Rats and lizards," she said, "but they come here anyway."

The cynicism of her remark stung Thornton. He looked away from her for a moment, rubbed his hands through his hair. "Could I use your bathroom?" he asked.

"Sure. It's the door right down the hall. To the left."
She watched him get up and lope down the hall to the
bathroom as she sipped her coffee. It tasted awful. *Must
be the milk in the coffee,* she thought. *I should have used
Coffeemate.* The milk was sour. *I'm getting so damned
sloppy,* she told herself, looking around the living room,
which was in a mess. She hadn't put away the dishes from
last night's dinner with Don. Lately, she'd had no energy
to clean up, and she stared at the vacuum cleaner standing upright in one corner. It had been there for two weeks.

It's the goddamn summer, she thought, *that sun, the
heat. It's just too much in Vegas, it burns everything out,
and it burns you out too.* She could see the bright light at
the edge of the blackout drapes, and if she opened those
drapes the sun would burst in and make it so hot that all
the air-conditioning in the world wouldn't help. It was
cool in the apartment now, but not too cool; her apartment faced south and west and she got the full brunt of
the sun from midday on.

The water flushed, and then Thornton came out of the
bathroom. He sat down again. "That feels better," he said.
"I walked about a block to get here. The cabbie let me off
at the wrong street, and I sweat so much lately. It was good
to wash my face off, wash my hands. I feel much better
now."

"That's good," she said. There was a lull in the conversation. She didn't want to drink any more of the putrid
coffee and he didn't seem to have anything to say.

"What have you been playing?" she asked.

"Some blackjack and craps. Played this morning, but
no luck at all. No luck. I lost eight hands in a row at the
tables in blackjack. Right from the start. From the minute
I sat down. The dealer had only 20s and blackjacks."

"Where'd you play?" she asked.

"At the El Capitan, but things got so bad I thought I'd

change my luck, try a couple of other casinos. I went to the Sands and wound up at the MGM Grand. No luck anywhere."

"That's the way things go sometimes," she said.

"Just brutal. After that last table at the Grand, I felt like shit. You ever feel that way? I mean, I was so depressed. Just tired and depressed. I just can't seem to be able to win, to get ahead."

"Maybe you ought to stop playing."

"Stop? I wish I could. But I have to get even. I have to."

He said it so insistently that she turned to look at his face. It looked drawn, and his eyes were bloodshot, with dark circles under them. "Maybe I can help you," she said.

"You? How?" He shifted his weight, turning to face her directly.

"I know this guy. He's a pro at the game. Really terrific. You ought to back him."

"Back him? Are you serious?"

"I'm being very serious," she said, picking up a pack of Kents and lighting one with a snap of a silver lighter, blowing out the smoke as she talked.

"What do you mean, back him?"

"Well, you let him play with your money. He wins and you work out something."

"Wins? What if he loses?"

"Or he loses. *You* win or you lose, right? But he's very good. I've played with him, and I won a lot of money."

"You backed him?"

"Sure, I backed him. Why shouldn't I back him if I can pick up a thousand here and there?"

"Does he always win?"

"I don't know if he always wins, because nobody always wins," she said, "but when I played with him, he won."

"You played with him, or backed him?"

"Both. Both. When I play with him, I give him the money, and when I backed him, sometimes he played by himself."

"And where were you when he was playing?"

"Around the casino. Or I went home, anyplace. It didn't matter to me where I was."

"How'd you know how much he won?"

"He told me."

"You just took his word?"

"Why not? He's an honest dude."

"What percentage does he take?"

"Well, you better speak to him about that. I guess you could both work something out."

"I never heard anything like that before."

"Well, probably not. But I live here and get to meet everybody. And I've seen blackjack players by the hundreds and he's as good as they come."

"If he's so good, why does he need backers?"

"You better ask him. I'm just making a suggestion."

"What's his name?"

"You want to speak to him?"

"Maybe."

"If it's maybe, never mind. When you want to speak to him, let me know, and I'll give you his name."

Thornton sat and pondered the situation. He was thirsty. He asked Diane if he could have something cool to drink and she got up and brought him a glass of Tab. He drank greedily, not realizing how thirsty he was. He felt almost dehydrated and had a second glass.

Then he sat awkwardly, wondering why he was sitting and talking to Diane. He guessed he wanted to get laid, but the losses and the heat of the day and the lack of sleep had sapped his desire for it. He needed more strength, or something. He felt so low. For an instant he wondered if it would be a relief if he did away with himself.

The stereo was on and the station had been playing pop tunes. Now it played a medley from *My Fair Lady*. Thornton closed his eyes during one of the tunes, then reopened them.

"I think I might just call him up, Diane. Are you sure he's that good?"

"I'm telling you, he's one of the best. I'd give him my money any day of the week."

"What I don't understand is why he needs a backer, if he's so good," said Thornton. "It's like racehorse touts; if they can pick winners, why are they touting?"

She shrugged her shoulders, got up, and wrote down Don's first name and his phone number on a piece of paper.

Thornton studied it, then put it into his wallet. He got up. "I'll give him a call. And maybe, well . . . I'd like to see you again. Will you be at the El Capitan tonight?"

"I might be. I don't know. But you can always reach me by calling my number and if I'm not in, leave a message on my answering machine. I'll get back to you."

Thornton walked to the door. He extended his hand awkwardly. "Good seeing you again," he said.

"Same here." She watched him open the door and step into the bright sunshine.

10

After Thornton left, Diane went into her bedroom and rolled a joint. She sat on her bed, smoking it slowly, letting the smoke stay deep in her lungs, hearing the music from the stereo. It was the wrong music to get high on, but she was too tired to go to the living room and turn it off.

She finished the joint and lay on her bed, kicking the covers off, and she thought of Thornton for a moment.

What a strange guy, she told herself, what a strange dude. It was weird the way he came to see her, and then took off that way. What did he want from her?

She was too tired to think about him and closed her eyes, drifting into sleep. In her dream, her mother was in the back seat of a car she was driving, holding her son in her lap. Diane drove down dark strange roads, but when she got to her destination and turned to speak to her mother and son, the back seat was empty. They were gone.

Diane woke with a start. She felt her mouth dry from the marijuana. The dream had shaken her up. She went into the bathroom and pulled off the bathrobe, turning the shower on. She let the hot water run upon her back and neck, let the heat calm her, and then, after several minutes of this constant pressure from the shower muzzle, she stepped out.

She selected a large yellow towel, monogrammed DJK, and wiped her body off slowly. Then she combed her hair, the ends of which were wet with water. They hung straggly, and she got out an electric blower and dried her hair, then left the bathroom and went to the kitchen.

She drank a glass of Tab. In the kitchen closet she found a bottle of Dewar's. She poured some into the glass and went into the living room, sitting on the couch again. The music was still on, playing more pop tunes. She got up and turned it off. Anything was better than that music right now, even silence. She leaned back on the sofa and closed her eyes, sipping the Scotch with her eyes shut tight.

Thinking. She thought of her son and mother, and of her first trip to Las Vegas to get her divorce six years ago. She'd been just a kid when she got off the Greyhound bus on Main Street, with her suitcase in one hand and the name of the lawyer to see in her purse.

Just a kid. And it was so hot that day. She still remembered it. What month was it? May. Yes, May, just after William was born, one month after to be exact, and there she was getting her divorce, Lance's money orders in her pocket, enough to pay for the divorce, but she had to fend for herself in Las Vegas for six weeks.

She called the lawyer immediately from a phone booth on Fremont Street. His office was a few blocks up, on Carson, and she went to see him before she did anything else, dragging her suitcase along. Her prim white suit was soaked with perspiration by the time she got there.

The lawyer was pleasant and calming, and he drove her to a small rooming house on South Sixth Street, where a number of his other clients, also women waiting out their divorce, stayed. There was a nice room for her, but it wasn't air-conditioned, and it was impossible to stay there during the daytime heat.

But she was in no position to seek better accommodations, and the very next day she went looking for work. Diane bought the two Vegas papers, the *Review-Journal* and the *Sun,* and called several numbers, checking out the jobs listed in the classified section. That day she found a job as a clerk at a drugstore on Charleston, near Maryland Parkway.

The pay was poor—$2 an hour—but her room cost only $24 a week, and meals weren't expensive—there were cheap restaurants around the area. But the best thing about the job was that the drugstore was air-conditioned.

So the weeks went on. She hardly spoke to the women in the rooming house. They were older than she. Diane was only nineteen at the time, and these women impressed her as coarse, hard, and unattractive. She went bowling with a couple of them once at the Showboat, and once to a dance at a local country-and-western joint on Boulder Highway, but she knew she was out of her element. It was not Diane's style to drink beer with pseudo-cowboys and be pawed by them while listening to corny jokes. And the bowling bored her.

After a while, Diane spent her evenings by herself, either reading or going to downtown casinos. The casinos, like the drugstore, were air-conditioned, and it was worth the effort of taking long walks or waiting for the bus just to bask in the cool air. May turned into June and the weather got progressively hotter. On July 8, she was due to appear in court, after the mandatory forty-four days of waiting, but that still seemed a long way off.

One night, instead of going to the downtown places, she took a bus ride to the Strip, looking out the bus window with wide eyes at the elegant hotels on Las Vegas Boulevard South. So this was what it was all about, she told herself, staring with wonder at the buildings and the crowds, clutching her purse in her lap.

It was early evening. The dying rays of sun mingled with the neon lights coming on and shining on the desert —a magic time in Las Vegas. Diane got off at Flamingo Road and walked over to the Bonanza, but it was strictly a sawdust joint like the casinos downtown. She wanted to see the elegance, if there was any, of Las Vegas.

Diane walked across the street to the Dunes, and went in. The lighting was soft and it was fairly dark inside, with a hushed atmosphere, so different from the downtown clubs with their bustle and noise. She walked to the women's room and looked at her face in the mirror, put on lipstick, straightened her clothes, and combed her hair. In the casinos, she circled the room, then, on an impulse, sat down at a blackjack table. Though she had seen the game played, she barely understood it. The few times she did any gambling were at a bingo game or a keno game, where she bought the 30¢ ticket.

There were two other players at the table, sitting at opposite ends. She sat in the middle, and a minute later a middle-aged man with a large brown mustache sat down next to her, to her left. He dropped a couple of $100 bills on the table and was given a variety of casino checks.

Diane took out a $10 bill from her purse with shaking fingers, and was given ten silver dollars. She put one on the betting box in front of her seat. The dealer told her the minimum bet at the table was $2, so she added another dollar and began to feel really nervous. An hour's work was being bet on a game she knew nothing about.

The dealer shuffled up, one of the men cut the cards, and he began to deal. She looked at her hand and asked for another card.

"Scrape the cards if you want another one. Scrape them toward you," the dealer told her.

Diane did it, awkwardly, and got too many points. She became flustered and didn't know what to do. The dealer took away her cards and her bet, annoyed with her for holding up the game.

She lost two other bets the same way, and was down to $4. The mustached man now took an interest in her play.

"No, dear," he told her, glancing at her hand, "don't ask for another card. You have 17 already."

"But he has a 9. He might have 19."

"Yes, dear, but you'll go over if you take another card."

She listened to him. The dealer had a 10 in the hole for 19 and she lost that bet also.

"I should have taken a card," she poutingly told the player, as she looked at the two silver dollars left on the table.

"I know," he said, "but you can't draw to 17. Aren't you going to make a bet?"

"No." The dealer didn't wait for her to make up her mind, but was already dealing the cards.

"How much did you start with?" the man asked, pushing his 20 under his checks.

"Ten dollars."

"Well, don't worry." He handed her two red checks, each worth $5. "Now, that'll make you even. Bet $2 again."

She did, and drew an 11. "Double down," said the man. She looked at him blankly.

"Here. Let me. You see, you can double your bet if you want to, if the first two cards are good." He turned over her cards, and took a red check and placed it next to her $2 bet. The dealer changed it, left $2 next to her original bet and gave her $3 in change. Then he threw a card on the turned-up cards. She looked at it. It was a 10, and she won that bet.

She listened to her adviser and he gave her more than advise. He began to make $5 bets for her, and slowly she built up the original $10 to $50.

A few minutes after she hit the $50 mark, the man looked at his watch. "I have to be going," he told her. "Good luck, honey."

Diane picked up the red checks and tried to give them back to him. "Don't be silly, dear," he said. "They're yours. We both won. Keep them."

And he was gone. She was stunned, and looked up to see the dealer staring at her, waiting for her to make a bet. She shook her head, and he kept dealing to the next player, then she gathered up the checks and coins and walked toward the front entrance of the casino. Then she realized she hadn't cashed in the checks, and had to ask a security guard where she could get her money. He directed Diane to the rear of the casino, to the cashier's cage. She was given a $50 bill for her play at the table, and she went home that night on the bus, her head spinning. She had made $40 in profits, and it took her three days of work to earn that much. There was more to Las Vegas than she had ever imagined.

The next night, she was back on that bus, going up the

Strip again. For the first time since she had begun work, the day had dragged. Two dollars an hour. It all seemed a waste of time, when so much money could be made for sitting at a table and being nice to a man.

She walked slowly through the Dunes, looking for that man with the mustache, but he wasn't around. She sat at a couple of blackjack tables, but nobody paid any attention to her, except a young dealer on the make. Diane went back to the rooming house that evening in poor spirits. A wasted night, and she had lost $8, plus her busfare. She decided to forget about gambling and concentrate on her job.

But late that Saturday afternoon, she left work and again took that bus to the Dunes. The tables were crowded, and she felt uncomfortable because a security guard was eyeing her. She left there and went across the street to the Flamingo.

At the Flamingo, she played at a $2 table, but it became filled with other women. Having lost a few dollars, she decided to leave, and got up, heading for the cashier's cage to turn in her checks. Distracted, she bumped into a man.

"Sorry," he said.

"Oh, I'm sorry."

"I was watching you play at the blackjack table. How'd you do?"

"I . . . uh . . . lost $30."

"You must have had terrible luck."

"Uh . . . yes."

The man she was talking to was short, about her height, but he was good-looking, with a nice set of teeth and dark, curly hair.

"Do you know how to play craps?" he asked.

"No."

"Are you in a hurry?"

"I was going back, to cash in these chips." She showed him two $5 checks.

"Well, if you're not in a hurry, how about playing some craps with me?" Seeing her uncertain face, he said, "Don't worry, you'll play with my money. Come on, I believe in beginner's luck. Maybe you'll be lucky for me."

They walked to the craps table in the rear of the casino.

"My name's Carlos. What's yours?"

"Diane."

"Diane, you're going to be lucky for me. I just know it. You ever feel anything like that, that you just know something good is going to happen?"

She didn't say anything, but walked with Carlos to the table. She stood awkwardly next to him, but he didn't make a move to take any money from his pocket. He merely raised his hand and was magically given $500 in checks.

Carlos tried to explain the game to her. He told her about line bets, place bets, come bets, odds bets, hardways, but it all went over her head. Diane was distracted by the crowded table packed with shouting men and couldn't concentrate on what he was saying. She was the only woman at the game, and from the start, Carlos was losing. He had already lost half the checks.

By the time Carlos held the dice, he had only a few left. He quickly sevened out.

"Now it's up to you, Diane," he told her, as the dice moved in front of her.

"What do I do?"

"Pick up two of them and throw them across the table to the other side. And pray for a 7 or 11."

She selected two dice, feeling their strange coolness and the bite of their corners. She shook them and threw them hard, and one flew over the table, hitting a man in the stomach. "Oh," she said to Carlos, "I'm sorry. Does that mean you lose?"

"No, it's no roll. Try again. Throw them a little easier."

She threw an 8, and watched as he put down the rest of his checks on the layout. He had none left in his rails.

"Now, numbers, Diane."

"What do you mean?"

"Anything but the 7. Anything but that number."

She threw a 6, then a 9, then another 9, 5, 4, 10, and finally an 8. She had bet a red check on the pass line for herself, and Carlos had put another on the back line for her. She now collected $12 in profits. But Carlos had collected a great deal, and the checks were filling up his rails again.

"Keep it up, Diane."

"I'll try."

She rolled a 7 and thought that she lost everything for Carlos, but it turned out to be a winner on the come-out roll, and she was given another red check, and the table whooped with joy. She didn't understand this game at all. *Didn't he say no 7?*

She threw a 4 on the next roll.

"Now numbers," he told her.

She rolled a hard 4 right back and the table went crazy. She was accumulating her own little stack of red checks, but not knowing why.

Diane had beginner's luck, all right. She held the dice for almost a half hour, making numbers and points. Slowly she began to understand what was happening. By this time her rails were filling with red checks, with a green $25 check mixed in. When her roll finally ended, the men at the table applauded and threw her kisses.

Carlos bought back his marker and they walked to the cashier's cage. He took all the checks, hers and his, and she thought, he'll give me nothing, he'll keep it all now. Diane watched him stack the checks on the counter, and get paid off with $100 bills, thirty of them. He had cleared a profit of $3,000, all on her roll.

Carlos counted out three of the bills and gave them to her. "Here you are, 10 percent commission. Is that fair?"

She was stunned. She never expected him to give her so much. Diane looked at the $100 bills. She had never owned one before.

"You're not disappointed with what I gave you, are you?" Carlos asked.

"Oh, no. Oh, no. Thank you very much. Thank you."

"Now, how about dinner?"

"I don't know . . . uh . . ."

"What do you mean, you don't know? Do you have to go somewhere?"

His words were spoken with a precise accent. "Are you here with your family?" he asked.

"No. I'm living here. You see . . ."

"Well, tell me the story over dinner."

He took her to the Candlelight Room, the gourmet room of the Flamingo, where they had steaks and champagne and petits fours and brandy and coffee. And there she told him about her marriage to Lance Darwin, the football star at Kansas University, about her life in Lawrence, about her widowed mother, and her son, about her cheerleading days at college, and the breakup and the divorce about to be consummated.

He listened soberly, smiling and frowning alternately at the good and bad parts. After supper he took her to a lounge show at the Sahara, and then dancing at the Landmark. It was a wonderful night, and she was a little drunk and tired when he brought her back to the Flamingo.

In his room, she undressed and he caressed her. They made love slowly. Carlos was very considerate and gentle, nicer to her than any man had ever been, including her husband. The next morning, they had breakfast at the coffee shop in the Flamingo, and then he put her in a cab for her rooming house.

Diane had his name and address in her purse, along with the information that he was married, and if she wanted to contact him, she was to write to his office in El Paso. He was half Mexican and half American, and his name was Carlos Robert Amaya. The following Monday she opened a bank account, depositing the $300. It was the first money she had been able to save since her marriage, because her husband had emptied out the bank accounts they held jointly, in his vain quest to make a professional football team.

On the day of her divorce, Diane, accompanied by her landlady, met her attorney in the courthouse. Hers was the first case on the calendar, and the room was empty except for the judge and a court stenographer. Diane was guided through her testimony by the lawyer, then stepped down. The landlady testified that Diane had resided continuously in Las Vegas for forty-four days and had not left the state during that period of time. And that was it. The judge signed the divorce decree, it was filed upstairs in the county clerk's office, and Diane received a certified copy. She was now a free woman.

She went back to the rooming house that afternoon and packed up, wondering if she should take the bus back to Lawrence or fly there, using her savings. She sat on the sofa bed and thought and thought, but somehow she couldn't get the energy to call either the bus terminal or the airlines.

Instead, she wrote a long letter to Carlos, telling him that she was looking forward to seeing him again and that she wanted to stay in Las Vegas for awhile, and asking him if he could lend her $500 so that she could find an apartment and get settled.

After writing the letter, she was tempted to tear it up. Diane realized that she was making a dangerous move— one that would plunge her into unknown territory, into a future she might find tempting but that was full of pitfalls.

Diane finally packed up, said goodbye to her landlady, and called a cab. She didn't head for a bus terminal or the airport but went down Fremont Street and found a cheap motel there. She checked in for the week to take advantage of the lower rate, which was the same as the room she had had. At last she was in an air-conditioned place. After putting away her things, she mailed the letter to Carlos, using the motel as a return address. His reply came five days later. In the envelope was a money order for $500. Diane put it into her bank account and then looked for both an apartment and an inexpensive car.

She found an apartment near Flamingo Road, a couple of blocks from the Strip, and bought a used Chevy. Now it was no longer necessary for her to take buses or walk in the heat of Vegas. She had wheels and was close to all the action.

She quit her job a week after getting the car, and by the time Carlos came to Vegas in September, she had met several other men—casual visitors—who came on junkets and who treated her the way Carlos had.

This visit, Carlos looked a little haggard. He told her his marriage was falling apart and he was having trouble in business. But he was generous as usual, and insisted that Diane keep the $500 and not consider it a loan. When he left that Sunday, he said he might not be back for quite a while.

Diane was sorry to see her friend and patron leave, but other men crowded her life. She also met women who lived similar lives in Vegas. And this was the life: she wasn't a prostitute, but she was one of that group of women who gambled with men, sometimes slept with them, and grabbed all the checks at the table they could. The term common in Vegas to describe these women was "chip hustler."

Diane bought all the garments necessary for her work. Large boots, with plenty of space to drop casino checks in, low-cut sexy dresses. She started to make big money, and one of her patrons, a Jewish businessman from Norfolk, Virginia, bought her a Lincoln Continental after a successful binge at the tables.

The businessman lost it all the next night, but she had her car, and after that a succession of Lincolns, which she traded in every other year. Her last one cost $12,000 and came with every possible option.

As the years went by, the men blurred, one into the other. Only Carlos stood out in her mind, along with whoever was her latest benefactor. Each year her expenses increased and she needed more and more money to keep going. She sent a check to Kansas every month, to support both her mother and her son.

As she sat in her living room with her eyes closed, she thought of all the years gone by, but they meant no more than leaves of a calendar. It was all abstract, all unreal, all lost in the smoke of time.

Diane opened her eyes. She decided to have another joint before she went out for the day.

11

Sitting in Manny Franks's room at the Sahara, Teddy Butler jiggled the glass of gin and tonic and watched the ice cubes move slowly among the lime slices. He looked up at Franks, who was dressed in a wild flowered shirt, white vinyl boots, and sharp flared-cuffed pants.

"So, when your cousin Bobby in LA told me about you, I figured I'd come and take a look, Teddy, listen to what you have to say." He cleared his throat. "You smoke dope?"

"Once in a while."

"Sniff coke?"

"Sometimes. But I deal, you know, and when you deal cards, you need a clear head."

"Really . . . so, tell me, Teddy, what's the scam?"

"Manny, it's simple. I deal the cards, right? And I got no options, right. I got to hit all 16s and stand on all 17s. Right?"

Manny Franks listened, patting his carefully combed hair.

"So, in the El Capitan, they deal all the cards open, because it's a four-deck game."

"Yeah, I know, I played there."

"So, I see what you have, right? Then I give you a signal —you know, if I have a bust card in the hole, I let you know that, so you don't bust yourself. And if I have a 7 or higher, then I let you know that. If I got a 10 or ace as my upcard, I have to peek at the hole card, right? That's when I let you know."

"Sounds good."

"It *is* good."

"You work it before?"

"Yeah . . . made some good bread with it."

"Who'd you work it with?"

"A few guys. None of them had real heavy bread, you know, except one, but he was a jerk. He cheated me on the payoff, so I got rid of him. I don't want problems and I don't want to get ripped off. All I want is a big score."

"What you figuring?"

"I'm thinking a hundred grand."

"Hundred grand? Shit, Teddy, how can you make that? The house has an edge in the fucking game, doesn't it?"

"Not if you know my hole card, it don't. We have the edge."

Franks lit a thin cigar, blew out some smoke, and thought about it.

"What about those one-way mirrors, and everything?," he asked. "The fucking pitbosses watch those games like hawks. I figure if you're talking in terms of one hundred G's, there's going to be some real heavy bread out on that table."

"Nothing to worry about. I got the pitboss and the floorman wired on my side. They're in on the scam."

"They're in on it?" Franks blew out more smoke. "I don't know. You got too many dudes involved in this."

"No, they just leave me alone for their cut. A couple of the dealers work it at the casino. It's a loose place."

"That's Balofsky's joint, isn't it?"

"Yeah, but he's in Detroit. The guys running it don't know shit."

"So, there's you, and two other dudes, right?"

"Yeah, three of us."

"Do I meet them?"

"No way. I deal with them. You deal with me."

Franks thought for a moment. "I don't know. The setup sounds . . . you know . . . involved."

"Look, it's clean as a whistle. It's clean and there's nothing to worry about."

"Yeah, what about the one-way mirrors? They got them, don't they? And they got cameras on the tables also. I seen them."

"The one-way mirrors . . . they're nothing. I don't worry about them, because the signal I give is perfect. No one can tell nothing, not from windows in the sky. No way."

"And what about the cameras?"

"No sweat. They can't tell what I'm doing."

"And what about this hundred grand? What do I see out of it?"

"Here's the deal. I got to split it three ways, plus your share. You get one share, I get one share, and the pitboss and floorman each get one share. It's got to be split that way, so if we make the hundred G's, that's twenty-five for each of us."

"Shit, man, you're giving away a whole bit. To win a hundred grand at the tables, man, that's work. That's heavy labor. They'll be all over us if we beat them out of that much. I can see it at craps, but not at twenty-one. Can't see it."

Teddy put down the glass, his mind spinning tales, weaving them in and out, trying them on for size.

"Tell you what, Manny. I can speak for the floorman. We can leave the pitboss out of this scam. The signal is so good . . . he won't know till it's too late. I'll just tell him you were running lucky . . . had a hot hand. They don't know how I do it anyway. So we'll talk about a three-way split. That's a better deal all around."

Franks was unmoved. "It sounds like real trouble to me. Too much of a risk, man. Too much. Now you're cutting out a dude who can blow a whistle. I don't know."

"Look," said Teddy, "you want in or out?"

"Hey, man, don't press me to the wall, man. I'm telling you how it's coming out, man. I don't want to fall to these fucking casinos, man. They're fucking sharks out here. And I gotta be super careful, the work I'm in. I'm just letting you know the situation."

Teddy sucked out the remains of the gin and tonic, and put the glass on the coffee table.

"Well, Manny, you don't want in, I can see that. So, I'm gonna split."

Franks eyed him. "Look, man, it's your scam, not mine. Four ways, then three ways, man, I just can't see it, you dig?"

Teddy was on his feet. "I gotta go."

"Keep cool, man."

Out in the hallway, waiting for the elevator, Teddy cursed himself. Son of a bitch, he got greedy in the room. And with some dude who wasn't a fucking liar like Thornton. This dude had been around—a drug dealer; you just couldn't bullshit him. No, you couldn't bullshit him and get away with it. Why the fuck did he bring in the phony floorman and pitboss? He was losing the whole deal because of his greed.

The elevator came and he rode it down to the main floor, then took it up again to Franks's floor and went down the hallway, knocking on Manny's door.

"Yeah?"

"It's me, Teddy."

The door opened.

"Let's rap about this a little more," said Teddy.

"Come on in."

Teddy sat down, and Franks offered him another drink. The dealer said no thanks, and watched as Franks sat down opposite him, pulling up a chair until the two men were only a few feet apart.

"So what's on your mind?" Franks asked.

"I been thinking. Let's work it another way. I'll split my share with my people, so we go into this fifty-fifty. Half and half. Right down the line, you and me."

Franks looked at the dealer, then lit a joint and paid attention to the smoke blowing around his head.

"Hey, man, you're full of shit, you know that?" Franks said, blowing out smoke as he spoke.

"Wait . . ."

"No, listen to my rap. Hear me out. Look, man, I don't know you and you don't know me, right? You were recommended, that's all. And I do some work with your cousin, so I came to hear your scam. You got your scam and I got mine. I didn't come up here to hear bullshit or to be jerked off. No fucking way I can be jerked off. This bullshit about floormen and pitbosses. I know the scam. Hey, man, I been around Vegas a while. You wanted to grab most of the bread. Cool, but not with me. Now you want half. But level with me, man, it's just you I'm dealing with, right? No fucking pitboss and all that shit. Right?"

Teddy didn't answer.

"All right, you don't have to say. Now let's level, OK? I'll go to your table, and I'll work it out with you, fifty and fifty. That's cool. You need my bread and I need your dealing. That's the way things work."

"That's what I said, fifty-fifty."

"All right. Now, what's the deal? How do I know what you're doing?"

"It's simple. I signal you every time I have to look at the hole card. It's a simple signal." The dealer took out a pack of DI cards and spread them on the coffee table.

"In our club they deal four decks, but it don't matter, because it's the same signal, no matter how many decks we use. You watch what I do."

He showed Franks the signal, and they went over it again and again.

They practiced for over two hours. Then, satisfied that they could work together, they made arrangements to play that night.

"Remember," said Teddy, "bet big and keep the big bets going. Don't go up and down with your bets, or they'll think you're a counter and then they'll really look you over. And go there sober, but order a couple of stiff drinks. Make it seem you're stoned or something, and just playing on hunches."

"I dig. That all sounds cool."

"Then we'll split the take later."

"What time does your shift go on?"

"Six. I get off at two in the morning."

"We'll meet at four. Over here."

"How about downtown?"

"I never go downtown," said Franks. "The best place is in a room, like this room. No eyes in this room. No one but us."

"I leave the casino wearing my dealer's outfit. I'll change first, then come here."

"Four give you enough time?"

"Between four and five. We got all the time in the world to count the bread, right?"

For the first time, Manny Franks smiled.

Outside, in the hallway, waiting for the elevator, the dealer whistled a Neil Diamond tune. Yeah, he thought, it didn't pay to be greedy. This was going to work out; he could feel it in his bones.

12

The television set in Steinberg's bedroom was on, and the Fletcher Jones Chevrolet commercial was in full swing, with Fletcher Jones in a leisure suit prancing around his cars with a microphone, talking about the incredible buys and creampuffs he had for sale. This one was $3695 and that one $4295 and this other one a low $2599. Could you believe those prices? In another scene, there was Jones again, with his warm smile, holding two puppies. That was the part that Steinberg particularly enjoyed, the warm, animal-loving side of Fletcher Jones. At that moment, Jones was all heart, all sincerity, ending his pitch with "Thank you very, very much."

Still, as good as Fletcher Jones was, he couldn't compare to Bob Glinski, the Datsun dealer, who would speak for about three minutes about his Datsuns in an accent that Steinberg generally couldn't understand. Glinski ended his pitches with a curt "Dank you." But maybe it was more sincere than Fletcher Jones. Glinski was not a man of emotion, and he probably meant that "Dank you."

Another favorite was Big Bob Albright, who always posed in front of his motor-parts store. Big Bob was not only sincere but bilingual, and occasionally he translated his pitch for his "Spanish-speaking friends."

The greatest shows in town, thought Steinberg. If they all performed at the Grand, he'd pay $15 to watch them— Jones with his dogs, Glinski just moving his lips, and Big Bob doing anything. It would be better than Edie Adams or Bob Goulet.

The movie came on again, and Steinberg shut off the set. He went to the kitchen for another glass of water. The day had been brutally hot, with the temperature at McCarran over a hundred degrees at six this morning.

He padded around the apartment in his shorts, his bare feet pressing into the gold carpet. He opened the refrigerator, which, thanks to some depraved decorator, was pink, but it was empty except for a couple of bottles of tonic water and a lime.

Time to dress and go out, he thought, time to get moving. He went back into the bedroom and selected his outfit, picking his clothes carefully. In front of the mirror he brushed his hair, opened his mouth to examine his teeth. Then he left the apartment.

The Pontiac was parked in the rear. He started it up and let it cool off just a bit. Getting a car with airconditioning had been a good move—better than that old Mustang that felt like a furnace day or night.

Steinberg cut down into Twain and headed for the El Capitan. The Strip was just ahead when he got to Paradise, and he could see the Dunes sign and the lights of the MGM Grand shining in all their lurid opulence.

He had some time to kill and drove slowly. Later on he'd meet this Mr. Thornton who had called him early that afternoon. He might be the backer Steinberg was waiting for, but he'd wait and see. Good old Diane had recommended Thornton. She was a sweetheart.

Steinberg left the car with the valet and went into the El Capitan's casino, casually looking around. A short, squat man with a cigar jammed in his mouth was in his way, and both men stared at each other, then moved on. The man's face was familiar; where had he seen him before?

Steinberg shrugged off the question and continued to walk around, looking over the people. He avoided the huge line that was snaking around the casino, all guests waiting to get into the showroom. Again his mind went blank as he tried to think of the performer they were panting to see. His mind was falling apart. Can't remember names, can't remember anything, he thought, except the point count at a single-deck blackjack game.

A drink would be welcome. He plopped down in the lounge and ordered a Wild Turkey, watching the twenty-one game going on below him. The dealer was sliding out the cards with quick moves at the $25 table, and the players, all supplicants, all beaten, sat draggy with bowed heads, taking their punishment. The dealer turned over a blackjack for the house, and two players instantly fled, grabbing their few remaining checks and running from the table. Steinberg smiled, thinking of his nights of bad luck, times when nothing went right for him, when the game could have been called "castrate Steinberg" instead of blackjack. He'd had his balls clipped any number of times, he remembered, as he paid the cocktail waitress for his drink. Any number of times. He sipped the bourbon and it tasted good, just the right taste for him tonight. He decided to order another—a double, this time.

He was thinking about leaving when he spotted Diane walking through the casino with a man who looked from side to side as if afraid someone would recognize him.

Diane came over to the lounge, waved to Steinberg, and introduced the man to him as Henry Porter. Porter was about forty-five or fifty, depending on which way he turned his head.

"Henry's in the furniture business in Grand Rapids; that's in Michigan," Diane informed Steinberg.

"That where Ford is from, isn't it?" Steinberg asked the furniture man.

"He was our congressman, now he's president," Porter replied.

"He's president now?" said Steinberg, feeling a little giddy from his drinks. "I didn't know that."

Porter looked at him quizzically. "You didn't know he was president?"

"How about a drink?" said Diane. "Don, sweetie, would you order a drink for me if I asked you?"

"Certainly."

"I'll get you one," said Porter, signaling for the waitress. "What do you want, Diane?"

"Cointreau," she said, pronouncing it cunt-row.

"All right, that's what you'll have."

"I want a double, though."

"Double," repeated Porter.

"On ice."

"On ice."

The waitress came over.

"Can I get you something?" Porter asked Steinberg.

"No, thank you."

Porter ordered the Cointreau and a glass of white wine for himself.

"Don's a physician," Diane told Porter.

"Oh . . ." Porter looked at Steinberg with interest.

"Yes," said Diane, "he's a surgeon." Don could see she was out of it.

"Well, doctor . . . I didn't get your name."

"Dr. Doom."

"Doom?"

"Yes, D, double O, and M. A lot of people here call me Doctor Dunes; they mix me up with the hotel."

"Henry is in the furniture business," said Diane.

"Yes," said Steinberg, "where is that, doctor?"

"No," said Porter, "I'm not a doctor."

"Oh," said Steinberg, "I'm sorry. I thought Diane said you were a doctor."

"You're the doctor," said Diane. "Don is a brain surgeon."

The drinks came. Porter paid for them and then asked again if Don wanted a drink.

"No," said Steinberg, "I don't drink. I have only one kidney."

"Oh," said Porter, "I'm sorry." Then he glanced at Steinberg's glass and again at his face.

"Well," Don said, "I've got to be going. I have a call to make."

Porter stood up. "Nice meeting you, doctor."

"Yes, nice meeting you," said Steinberg, bowing formally.

"Don's a brain surgeon," Diane repeated, as Steinberg kissed her on the cheek. "He's a wonderful doctor. He saved my child . . . He's wonderful."

"I must be going, however," said Steinberg, "I have a call to make. Diane, I have to call on Mr. Thornton down at the Horseshoe."

"He called you, did he?"

"Yes, he's in very bad shape. Needs my help badly." He nodded gravely to Porter and left the table.

The two men sat in the booth of the Horseshoe Coffee Shop, waiting for the busboy to put down some iced waters. Thornton examined the menu.

"You eaten yet?" he asked Steinberg.

"No, but I'm not hungry. I'll just have coffee."

"So," said Thornton, "Diane spoke highly of you. She said you could really play blackjack."

"Well, I can play the game."

"How'd you meet Diane?" Thornton asked.

"At a blackjack table."

"That's as good a place as any. I met her at a craps table. Just hang around the tables and you meet Diane."

"She's all right," Steinberg said.

"She's a hooker, isn't she?"

"No. She's not a hooker."

"What would you call her?"

"Why call her anything?"

"That's a point. Why call her anything?"

The waitress came over and Thornton ordered two coffees and sweet rolls for himself. Steinberg drank some water. He was thirsty as hell; couldn't seem to get enough water.

"So," said Thornton, "what's the deal?"

"It depends on you. What kind of money do you have to play with?"

"Before we get into that, I'd like to ask you a couple of questions. You don't mind, do you? You don't mind, either, if I call you Don?"

"No. Why be formal?"

"Good. Call me Lee. OK? Fair enough?"

"Sure."

"OK. A couple of questions. I've been around race-tracks, and around a lot of gambling joints. So I want to ask you, if you play such a good game of twenty-one, why do you need a backer?"

"Because I can make money for myself and my backer. It's that simple."

"But why don't you just play by yourself?"

"I could do that, in a nickel or quarter game, but what I'm looking for is a dollar game, a $100 table. I want to make it really big at those tables."

"With my money."

"That's right, with your money. But I can beat them."

"*Think* you can, or *can* you?"

"I can beat them."

"What you're saying is, you can always win? Is that what you're telling me?"

"No, I didn't say that. I can beat them, that's what I'm saying. If I play for any period of time, I'll have the edge on the house. I'll win. Over a short period of time, one session or two or three, I may lose, even take a bad beating. But I have the edge all the time. It's the same way with a casino, on games; there they have the edge. They can have losing sessions, but over the long pull they win."

"Yes," said Thornton, "but the casino has one other advantage that you don't have. They have unlimited money to ride out the losses."

"That's called the principle of gambler's ruin," said Steinberg. "But we can overcome that with the right stake."

The coffee arrived, with the sweet rolls. Thornton selected one, and offered the others to Steinberg, who shook his head.

"You know all about gambling, don't you?" Thornton asked.

"Sure. I make a living at it now."

"And you're telling me that you want a backer because you want as big a bankroll as the house?"

"No, I didn't say that either. We can't have that big a stake. I just want enough to sustain a bad run. If I can hold out, I can beat the game."

"You keep talking about beating the game and having the edge. I thought the house always had the advantage."

"Not in blackjack."

"No, why not?"

"You know the basic game, right? It's a simple game. Picture cards count as 10s, the ace is either 1 or 11 at the player's option, and all the other cards equal their spots. The thing is not to go over 21, not to bust, or you lose, right?"

"You're not telling me anything I don't know," said Thornton.

"Well, besides that, there's a basic strategy. If the dealer shows a 2 to a 6 as an upcard, you want to let him bust first, because he has to draw on all hands of 16 or less. He must, right?"

"Again, you're not telling me anything new."

"What I'm telling you is that if you count the cards as they come out, you realize that the composition of the remaining deck changes. The more large cards that come out, the less favorable the deck is to the player. The more small cards that come out, the more favorable. The deck changes from favorable to unfavorable and back again, depending on the cards already dealt. And it doesn't matter if it's a single deck or four decks. The composition of the deck continually changes."

"You read that in some book?"

"It's in all the books. Now, my theory is this. The dealer has only one advantage over the player. If the player busts first, he loses, even if the dealer subsequently busts. Once the player goes over 21, he loses the hand. The player has all the other advantages. He can split any pairs he wants, he can double down on any two cards, and he gets 3 for 2 for having a blackjack. That, together with the card count, is the way I beat the house. I play the right strategy for all card-count situations, and I vary my bets, and I don't make a wrong play."

Steinberg paused, and looked at Thornton.

"Yes," said Thornton, "I'm listening."

"So, if I alter my bets, and increase them when the deck is favorable, I always maintain a slight edge over the house. When the deck is unfavorable to me, I lower my bet to a minimum bet. I do to the casino what it does to the players at all the table games."

"Well, a lot of people have read the same books," said Thornton. "How come they haven't put the casinos out of business?"

"Reading about the game and playing it correctly are two different things. I've played for a long time. I keep control of my game. I don't go crazy during a game. And I can do things that other players can't. Like figuring out the hole card of a dealer, or getting a dealer to cooperate with me."

"You mean a cheating dealer?"

"No, just one that you toke the right way. He wants you to win so he can win that tip. He helps you in little ways. He sometimes gives away the value of his hole card, whether it's a bust card or a 7 or higher. It all adds up."

Steinberg paused again and drank some coffee. It was good coffee.

"I came out here because of a dealer," said Thornton. "I had a dealer who was supposed to work with me."

Steinberg leaned back and listened carefully to what Thornton was saying.

"You mean, cheat the house?" Steinberg said.

"Yes. We played once before, and he gave away his hole card to me. We made a killing together. But something happened. The guy chickened out or something. I never did find out. But he won't work with me anymore."

"Where was this?"

"At the El Capitan. It doesn't matter now, because if I still had him, I wouldn't be talking to you tonight. I'd be at the tables there, making a fortune."

Steinberg finished his coffee. "Well," he said, "what do you say, Lee?"

"About backing you?"

"That's it."

"What kind of split do you want?"

"Fifty-fifty."

"For backing you? No way."

"What are you offering?"

"I'm offering nothing till I see the way you play. But I'd say 10 percent."

"I wouldn't play for 10 percent."

"Then we have no deal."

"Fair enough."

Thornton worked on his second sweet roll. He looked up at the younger man, perhaps ten years younger, with his straight brown hair and blue eyes, but the eyes looked older than the face. If he'd have to guess, he'd guess that those eyes had seen a lot of things. "We'll compromise," said Thornton. "As long as we're here, we might as well work out some kind of deal."

"I'm listening."

"But why don't we do some playing first? I'll back you and we'll play a little. How about in this casino?"

"The Horseshoe's a good place. It's single-deck."

"Let's go then. Let's do a little playing."

An hour later, they left the Horseshoe and walked to the parking garage for Steinberg's car. They had won a little over $200, playing together in a nickel game. They played together at the same table, and during the course of the game, Thornton continually asked Steinberg questions about correct play, whether to double down or split pairs or stand or hit. He did what Steinberg told him to, and kept winning. "All right, I'm convinced," said Thornton, as Steinberg drove down Casino Center Drive, heading for the interstate highway.

"I told you I can beat them."

"I said I was convinced. You play a good game. I could tell that you really know the game."

"Well, let's make a deal."

"Twenty-five percent."

"No, it's too low."

"Look," said Thornton, "I went up from 10 percent to 25 percent."

"I know. But I want at least a third."

"A third? That's a big nut."

"Right now it's about $70 of what you're holding in cash from our win. That leaves $130 that you wouldn't have made by yourself."

"Peanuts."

"But if we played with quarter checks, that would be $650 as your share, and if we played with $100 checks, that share would be worth $2,600. That's not peanuts."

"It's not peanuts, I agree. But I don't want to give away that much. What if you win, then you lose? You don't pay for the losses, do you?"

"No."

"Then I'm left holding an empty bag."

"Let's think optimistically. Look, we'll count each night as a separate session. The whole night. If I win, let's say at one table and lose at another, we deduct the losses from the wins. After the whole night, we'll split. Look, I can waste a whole night and not win anything."

"Yes, but I take the losses."

Steinberg turned onto Interstate 15. "We could keep this up all night," he said. "Do we have a deal or not?"

"Where are you going?"

"To the Strip. To one of the big hotels."

"You won't take less than one-third?"

"No. Look, I'm not playing games. That's all I'll take. Period."

"All right, it's a deal. You want to go to the El Capitan?"

"No, they have a four-deck game. Let's play single-deck."

"Where?"

"A big hotel. We could start at the Hilton."

"All right, let's go."

Thornton hadn't made any move to give Steinberg his share of the $200, but Steinberg thought, *I'll wait. I'll be a little patient with this dude. Just a little patient.* He could see that it was going to be hard work getting this guy to give out money. Hard work.

13

Steinberg and Thornton entered the Hilton casino, a huge, cold room. The predominant color was blue, with the dealers in blue uniforms, the table layouts covered in blue felt. Blue and cold.

The Hilton casino was a place where a player could go from table to table and pit to pit, where he could remain anonymous. Steinberg had played there a few times before, when he went in to see the lounge shows, which featured performers like B. B. King and Wilson Pickett. For two drinks, Steinberg felt, it was the best buy in town.

This was Glenn Campbell's week at the Hilton's main showroom. Campbell was a good draw, and the casino was filled with people who had come out of the midnight show. But he was nothing compared to Elvis Presley. When Elvis played the Hilton, the whole town was covered with posters. For the King. That was his name in Vegas, the King. Steinberg had seen the faces of the women waiting on line for the Presley show. There were miniature orgasms up and down the line as the women squirmed, squealing like piglets, waiting to see ELVIS!

Tonight Steinberg's mind wasn't on the performers. He was looking for the right table to start his journey into

Big Numberland. Yes, he was going after that Big Number.

He picked a table far from the main part of the casino, in a pit that had just been opened for the showroom crowds filtering through the casino. It was a $25 table, and Thornton took out $2,000 in cash.

"Two thousand dollars change," said the dealer, catching the attention of the floorman, who came over to watch the money being counted and the checks given to the player.

"How do you want it, sir?" the dealer asked Thornton.

"A couple of hundred in quarters, the rest in hundreds."

"Right you are." The dealer counted out the checks, broke them down into stacks and recounted them, then slid them over to Thornton, who gave some to Steinberg, while placing two quarter checks on his and Steinberg's betting boxes. They sat in the two end seats, with Steinberg in the third baseman's seat, the last seat the dealer would deal to. No one else was at the table.

The dealer took up the cards and shuffled them with smooth motions, then gave them to Thornton to cut. The floorman stood at the edge of the table, near the first baseman's seat, watching the game.

After fifteen minutes of play, they were down $100.

"This is boring," said Thornton, as the cards were being reshuffled. "Let's hit this table. Bet the blacks, Don." They each put out $200 as their neutral bet. Thornton was dealt a blackjack immediately. "Just knew it was coming," he said. "Dealer, how about a drink at this table?"

They played on. Thornton followed Steinberg's lead in betting, raising his bets when Steinberg did, and lowering them at the same time he did. And he kept asking Steinberg's advice about various plays. Steinberg told him to double down on a soft 17 against the dealer's 3, and to split 6s against a dealer's 7, both moves that Thornton would never have made. But the bets turned into winning ones. They played at the table for another half hour and left ahead almost $2,000. Thornton had two drinks and was already swaying slightly on his feet. But his pockets were bulging with checks.

"I'll cash in and we'll start with cash again," he told Steinberg. "It's luckier that way."

"Whatever you say. You want to take a break?"

"No, how about you?"

"A little break." They went into the Hilton's coffee shop. Don had coffee and some fresh fruit. Thornton had nothing. He sat restlessly, waiting to get back to the tables.

"You play an amazing game," he told Steinberg. "I never would have doubled down the times you did. You really know the game, I'll say that for you."

Steinberg drank his coffee slowly, trying to relax. This was his big chance to get that stake, and he didn't want to blow it by being wound up.

They went to another blackjack pit this time and sat down at a $100 table, occupied by a woman in her sixties who sat alone at the table in the first baseman's seat, diamonds sparkling from every finger. She was slightly tight and bet a $100 check each time, never varying. It didn't seem to matter to her whether she won or lost. She'd just put another check on the box.

Steinberg and Thornton took the same two seats they had had at the other table. Thornton immediately ordered drinks and put another $2,000 on the table. They increased their normal bet to $500 and went to $1,000 when the deck was favorable. When it was unfavorable, they dropped to $200. It was the biggest game of blackjack Steinberg had ever played.

The cards were good. The dealer busted on four consecutive hands. Thornton kept drinking, switching to straight Russian vodka on ice. Steinberg kept the black coffees going. He wanted his mind to stay clear. He didn't want to miss anything.

The checks piled up, higher and higher. At one point, Thornton, who was getting groggy from the liquor, got up and went to the cashier's cage to cash in a pile of black checks. "Cashed in ten thousand," he whispered to Steinberg, as he returned to the table. Thornton's breath was sour from the liquor. He began giggling.

"Take it easy," said Steinberg. But Thornton was now in a world of his own. He bet $1,000 on the very next hand, just when the deck was at its worst for the players. They lost that hand and the next two, all $1,000 bets on Thornton's part.

The profits were being drained away. "Let me make the bets," Steinberg said.

"No, I know what I'm doing. It's my money."

"Lee . . ."

"Look, you play your hands and I'll play mine."

By now, Thornton couldn't even add up the cards. He gulped down a double vodka, which was immediately replaced by another. He looked at his cards and had to ask Steinberg what to do. The cards were just blurs to him.

"Go and take a break," said Don. "I'll play alone for a while."

"No . . . I want to play. What do I do with these cards?"

"You have 20. Stand."

"No, I want to split the 10s."

"It's bad. Just stand."

"The dealer has a 6. It's a good split."

"It's no good. The count is bad," he whispered to Thornton.

"What's the count?" Thornton asked, almost shouting

the words. Steinberg flinched. Already a couple of floormen were watching the game.

Thornton split the 10s anyway, hit on the first and got a 2 for 12.

"Now what do I do?" He gulped down the remains of the new drink.

"Do whatever you want to."

"Hey, you're the expert. I'm paying for your advice."

"Take it easy, will you? Stand."

"OK."

He got a 3 on the other 10.

"Stand on that, also," he told Thornton.

The cocktail waitress came over. Thornton ordered a black coffee this time, and some aspirins and water.

The dealer waited as Thornton looked at his 13 on the second split.

"I have a hunch, Don," he said. Thornton scraped for a hit, and got a 4 for 17. Then he slid the cards under the checks. The dealer turned over a 5 for 11. Steinberg winced. Down the drain. He bought another 5 for 16 and busted with a jack. Thornton's buy had saved both hands.

The woman got up after this play, leaving them alone at the table, except for the five men in the pit watching the game.

The black coffee came. Thornton finished it, had the aspirins and the water. "That helped," he said to Steinberg. "Don, doesn't the dealer remind you of someone?"

"Who?"

"Teddy, at the El Capitan."

"Who?"

"That son of a bitch, Teddy."

"Who's Teddy?"

"That dealer I told you about."

Steinberg nodded. Thornton had been pointing out a new dealer at the table, who was shuffling up.

Thornton now spread checks over the layout, playing all six hands by himself, a thousand a hand.

"This is crazy," said Steinberg.

"We got them by the short hairs," Thornton said. He looked flushed and exhilarated. Steinberg wondered if he was really that drunk.

Thornton cut the cards. The dealer had a 4 as an upcard. "You're fucked," Thornton told the dealer. "We got you by the balls this time." He turned over the first hand. A blackjack. The dealer paid him $1,500. On the next hand he turned over a 5, 3—an 8.

"Double down."

"Don't," said Steinberg, but Thornton motioned him away. Thornton felt absolutely free of worry right now. This was it, he thought, action . . . life . . . winning.

He showed Steinberg the card he bought, a 7 for 15. "We'll win anyway," he told Steinberg. "They can't beat us anymore." He stood on the other hands, and the dealer busted his hand. He paid out $6,000 to Thornton.

The cards were taken away from the dealer by the pit-boss. He counted them and then examined the fronts and the backs, holding up the game. A new deck was put into play. The cocktail waitress came over. The men ordered two black coffees.

While the new deck was examined and reshuffled, Thornton put out six bets of $1,000 each. He got the cards to cut, and cut them as thin as he could. "Thin means we win," he told Steinberg, finishing off the coffee and ordering another. His face had lost its color. The dealer's upcard was a 7. Thornton looked at his first hand, then showed it to Steinberg. "What do I do?"

"Hit."

"Not double down?"

"Just hit."

"What's the count?"

"There is no count." Steinberg could feel his own face redden. The bastard kept talking about a count; it was trouble, all right. That word was poison to a blackjack pitboss.

Thornton hit and got a 6 for 20. "I told you I should have doubled down," he said. He played all the hands, asking Steinberg's advice, sometimes taking it, sometimes not. He couldn't seem to do anything wrong.

The dealer had an 8 in the hole for 15 and busted again. The cards were taken away from the dealer as he made his payoffs. Steinberg watched the men in the pit uneasily. He knew that the fact that he was helping Thornton and Lee's constant mention of the count had alerted the entire pit. There were now six men behind the table, watching Steinberg and Thornton.

"I'm cashing in some more," Thornton told Steinberg, loping away toward the cage. By the time he came back, a new dealer was on the scene, with a new deck of cards that he shuffled over and over again.

"How much did you cash in?" Steinberg asked.

"Enough." Thornton loosened his tie and collar and spread the money out on the layout, all $6,000 in $100 checks. This time he lost $2,000 on the round. Again, he put out $6,000, and the cards were reshuffled.

The dealer dealt himself an ace. "Insurance?" he asked Thornton.

Thornton shook his head without looking at any of the cards. The dealer peeked. No blackjack. Thornton turned over two blackjacks in a row. The cards were just incredible. The dealer had a 6 in the hole for a soft 17 but had to stand, and Thornton once more won all the bets.

"I feel sick," he told Steinberg. "Where's the bathroom?" he asked the dealer.

"To your right, past the slots."

"I don't know if I can play anymore," Thornton said. He got up and pushed the remaining checks into his pockets. "Wait here for me," he told Steinberg, "I'll be right back."

"You need any help?"

"No, Don. Just feel sick. I'll be all right. Be right back."

"I'll be at the cashier's cage. No sense staying here."

"OK, meet you there. Be back in a minute."

Steinberg walked over to the cage and stood there, waiting. One of the men who had been in the pit came over. "I'd like to talk to you," he told Steinberg.

"I'm listening."

"We don't want you to play blackjack in this casino again."

Steinberg didn't say anything.

"And that goes for your friend also."

"You're barring us?"

"That's right. We don't want to see you at those tables again. You understand?"

Steinberg stared at the floorman, who was in his thirties, suave, hair cut in mod fashion, wearing a fashionable suit with wide lapels. He wanted to say something, but what was there to say? He turned away and stood closer to the cage, then paced around the area. He waited for fifteen minutes, but there was no sign of Thornton.

Steinberg headed in the direction of the men's room, looking for him, but he wasn't in the casino. He went into the bathroom, and looked around. No one was in the stalls, and he wasn't at the urinals.

He could feel his skin crawl. Steinberg went outside and saw a row of cabs waiting, but no sign of Thornton. He probably took a taxi and disappeared, that son of a bitch.

The parking-lot boy came over, and Steinberg handed

him his ticket and asked if he had seen a man answering Thornton's description come out of the casino. The boy shook his head and went for Steinberg's car.

Steinberg cut back to the El Capitan at high speed. He called Thornton's room from the casino, but there was no answer. He waited near the front entrance, looking for him, then called the room again. Still no answer. Steinberg took the elevator to the third floor, found Thornton's room, and banged on the door, but no one answered. He banged again, harder, attracting the attention of a couple of people passing by.

Steinberg went downstairs and wandered around the casino floor, looking for Thornton. He looked in the coffee shop and the steakhouse, and in the men's room. No sign of him anywhere. He called the room again. Still no answer.

Finally he went home. Steinberg had nothing to show for this whole evening but a headache. *That son of a bitch,* he thought, parking the car, *I'll get my share from that bastard tomorrow.*

14

On Eastern, near Vegas Valley Drive, Diane stood in the early-morning darkness next to her silver Continental Mark IV, which was parked at the side of the road.

Milner, on his way home from the El Capitan, saw the Continental's rear reflectors and then saw the young woman waving. He came to a stop. "What's the trouble?" he shouted as Diane came over to his Porsche. He decided not to get out of the car. You never could tell what was going on in Vegas.

"Hi," said Diane. "I ran out of gas or something. Can you give me a lift to the station?"

Milner examined her and thought she looked vaguely

familiar. He had seen her before, probably at the El Capitan. He hesitated, then opened the door. "Sure, come in."

"Thanks. Thanks, really. All the stations around here are closed, and I'm wearing high heels, my platforms." She giggled. "And I'm stoned—it's a bad combination. If you could get me to a gas station . . . There should be one open somewhere. You live here in Vegas?"

"Yes, been living here a long time. I know where one is open." Milner made a U turn on Eastern and followed it to Charleston, then made a right turn.

"Where are we going?" Diane asked.

"Just down the street. There's one open near the Showboat. It's open twenty-four hours. When the gas shortage first came, you paid about ten cents more a gallon there than anywhere else, but they were open all the time." He offered a cigarette to Diane, who took it. He awkwardly tried to snap open his gold lighter, but then settled for the car lighter.

Diane dragged in deeply. "Thanks."

"That's all right."

"That was really nice of you. I appreciate it."

"That's OK."

They sat silently, as the Porsche whizzed along Charleston Boulevard.

"You look like someone I know," said Diane. "You ever go into the Grand?"

"A few times."

"Maybe I saw you there. I have this friend, Don . . . you know? And I asked him what he thought of the Grand, when it first opened, you know? He said it was another blight on the earth."

"Is that what he said?"

"Yes."

He could see she was laughing.

"I guess I'm stoned," Diane said.

"On what?"

"A little thisa, a touch of thata . . ."

"You live here, I guess?"

"Yes, another sucker living here."

"Why do you say that?"

She didn't answer.

They were at the station. Milner pulled in, and then, leaving the motor on, stepped out. Then he opened the door again and asked Diane if she was sure it was just that she was out of gas.

"Yes, I checked the gauge. The mother eats gas like it's going out of style."

Milner asked for a gas can, and had to leave a $5 deposit as well as pay for two gallons of gas. He carefully wedged the gas can into the trunk of the car.

"How much was it?" asked Diane.

"A $5 deposit for the can."

"No, I mean for the gas. I want to pay you for it."

"Oh, that's all right."

"No, really."

"It's just a buck and a quarter. Forget it."

"No . . ." She opened her purse as he cut across Boulder Highway. An oncoming car jumped the light and forced him to stop the Porsche short. Diane fell against Milner, and a shower of casino checks dropped out of her purse. "I'm sorry," she said.

"No, it was my fault. Wait . . . when we get back to your car, I'll help you find them." He spotted a couple of El Capitan checks on the seat. "You play much at the El Capitan?" he asked her.

"Yeah, I sort of like the place . . . Hey, what's your name?"

"Harry. What's yours?"

"Diane."

He cut down Charleston, heading for Eastern Avenue.

"I've seen you somewhere," she said.

"I work at the El Capitan. You may have seen me there."

"What do you do?"

"I run the place."

"You're kidding."

"Yes," he said, "I'm just kidding. I work in the back office."

Milner slowed down as they approached Vegas Valley. "Well, there's your car, still intact," he said.

Milner pulled up behind the Continental and went to get the gas can. Diane got out and opened the gas cap, and Milner poured the gas into the thirsty tank.

"Try it now," he said.

"Yes, I should. Yes." She tottered on her high shoes to her car and opened the door and got in, leaving the door ajar. The motor coughed and turned a few times, then caught.

"Well," said Milner, "that's that. Hey, how about those checks all over my floor? Come on, I'll help you find them."

"The hell with them. You keep them for me."

"No . . ."

"Listen," she said, coming out of the car, tottering again, nearly falling on the rough asphalt surface. "Listen," she said, "I'm going to have some coffee or something. You want some coffee?"

"I never turn down coffee."

"Follow me, then. I'm just a couple of blocks down the street. Just follow me."

"The coffee is lousy, isn't it? I can tell; you haven't touched it."

"Well . . ."

"It's just because I'm stoned, you see. That's the reason."

The cup with the coffee was in front of Milner, who sat at the dinette table across from Diane. Her long light-brown hair hung in disarray, part of it covering one eye.

"Why are you stoned?" he asked.

"That's a good question, you see, because I'm not always stoned. That's the truth, so help me God. Cross my heart and hope to die." She crossed her heart. "That's the truth," she said in a lower voice.

"You seem unhappy," he said.

"You have a kind face. Did anyone ever tell you that?"

"No," said Milner. "Most of the time, when I meet people, they think I'm tough. I'm supposed to be a mean son of a bitch."

"No," she insisted, "they have you all wrong. You're not mean. Are you?"

"Sometimes. It's the business. You understand?"

"I guess so." Her eyes looked blank. "No, I don't understand."

"It's the gambling business. You understand? You have to be hard in this business."

"Life is hard. Everything's hard."

"That's true." Milner lit another cigarette. Diane was smoking the one he had given to her a couple of minutes before. "That's very true, yes," said Milner. "Life is hard."

"I don't have to be a genius to figure that out," said Diane. "That's just the way things are."

"And right now, you're unhappy. You don't mind me asking, do you . . . why you're so unhappy?"

"It's a long story. Actually, it's one story piled on another, you know? It's a lot of long stories, like the way kids stack building blocks. That's the way my life is, one story piled on top of another . . . Maybe you want a drink?" she asked. "I see you're not going to drink the coffee."

"All right, a drink. Will you have one with me?"

"Sure, why not? I'm stoned enough. One more drink won't hurt . . . or help. What do you want to drink?"

"Anything."

"How about some Scotch? J&B. That means, 'Jewish Booze,' that's what this guy I knew from Norfolk called it. He was Jewish. Are you Jewish?"

"No. What about yourself?"

"Me? I'm a Wasp. My family . . . they're Okies who moved to Kansas when the dust bowl was . . . you know, in the thirties. The rest of my relatives moved to California, but my folks went to Kansas. That's where I'm from. From Lawrence, Kansas. You know where that is?"

"I've heard of it. It's a college town, isn't it?"

"Yes, I'm a college girl. No shit." She was on her feet, tottering still in her platforms. Then she kicked off her shoes, sending them one by one into the base of the refrigerator. Suddenly she was much shorter, much more fragile, thought Milner. He watched her open the closet doors of the kitchen and pull out a bottle of J&B. She brought two glasses to the table. "How do you want it?"

"With some water."

"OK. OK." She brought one glass to the cooler and pushed the white nozzle until water filled a quarter of the glass.

"Is that good?" she asked.

"Just right."

"Help yourself to the Scotch."

"You having some?" he asked.

"Sure. About so much." She indicated about two fingers'

worth on the glass. He poured out the drinks. "Well," she said, "we should drink to something, don't you think?"

"We could drink to your car," he said. "I'd never have met you if it wasn't for your car."

"No, I don't want to drink to cars. I want to drink to something else."

"You name it."

"No, it'll be secret. Let's drink to something secret."

"Fair enough."

"We'll each make a wish," she said.

"A secret wish?"

"All wishes should be secret," she said. "Otherwise, if you tell them to people, they just laugh at you."

He stared at her, lifted the glass, but couldn't think of any wishes. He drank some of the Scotch down. It tasted good with the cool water. "Did you make a wish?" he asked.

"Oh, yes. I had to. You know why?"

"Why?"

"Isn't it true, isn't it, in life . . . I mean, isn't it true, that you never get what you want? But what you don't want, I mean, it's there in spades. It's all over the place."

"That's so."

"You don't think I'm talking bullshit?" she asked.

"No."

"Like, there's this guy I like . . . I really like him, you know. I dig him . . . and you know, it's no good. He looks at me like I'm . . . like I'm part of the furniture, or something. Do you know what I mean?"

"I know that feeling."

"You ever felt it?"

"Sure."

"You feeling it now?"

"No, not now. There's no one I really want now."

"There's someone I want. I want him so bad. But he sees through me, you know. I mean, what am I? What am I? I'm nothing, just nothing." She tightened her mouth, then spoke again. "I even have a kid, and he doesn't live with me. I don't have the nerve to bring him here, make a home for him with me." She stopped talking. "I'm talking too much. I'm stoned."

Milner put his hand on her arm, and she stared at him. Her makeup looked wrong in the harsh kitchen light.

"You are a kind man, you know that?" she said.

"No, not really."

"Anyway . . ." She yawned. "I'm so tired. I'm going to sleep. You want to stay over?"

"Look . . ."

"Are you married? Is that it?"

"No, that's not the point."

"You can stay if you want."

She got up and went into the bathroom. Milner looked around the living room. He lit another cigarette. When she came back into the living room, she was wearing a blue nightgown.

"Come on," Diane said, "the bedroom's over there."

He took off his clothes and slid into bed. She got into bed and he put his arms around her. She had her back to him, and within a couple of minutes her breathing slowed down and she was asleep.

Milner disengaged his arms. He felt awkward and foolish, naked in bed with this sleeping stranger. He tried to sleep but couldn't. Gradually he moved away from her, got out of bed, dressed, and left the apartment.

When Milner pulled up in front of his own house, he realized that he still hadn't returned the gas can. Well, he'd send someone over tomorrow from the hotel. And there were still a couple of El Capitan quarter checks on the carpeted floor. He pocketed them. He'd return them to Diane the first chance he got. But then, he realized, he didn't even know her last name and he couldn't remember where she lived, exactly.

Well, he figured, she plays at the El Capitan. When he saw her there, he'd return them to her. He could barely drag his body into his house. He was really beat.

Friday

15

Milner looked at the clock in his office. It was late afternoon, almost four o'clock. He got up and went to the washroom and looked at his face in the mirror. His eyes were really bloodshot and his face was puffier than ever. *I look like hell,* he told himself as he washed his face, letting the cold water run over his eyelids. He dried his hands and face and went back to his desk.

He picked up his private phone and dialed the number in Denver at the place Mary was staying. The phone rang and rang, but no one answered. It wasn't a good sign, but what the hell could he do, sitting here in his office, imprisoned by fatigue and his work.

There was a knock on the door, and Chet Gardner, the credit manager, came in. He had a deep suntan and his white hair was combed down and glistened with oil. Chet put several sheets of paper on Milner's desk, sat down, and took a deep breath. "I brought all the figures on the junkets, Harry."

"Good."

"That's what you wanted, wasn't it?"

Harry shook his head, lighting a cigarette.

"Anything wrong, Harry?"

"No, nothing wrong. I'm meeting with Moe and some

interested parties, and I want to be up to date on all the figures."

When Milner first met Chet Gardner, Chet was the assistant credit manager of the Strip hotel where Milner was assistant president. Both were anxious for a move up, and when Milner got the job at the El Capitan, he took Chet along with him. Gardner was someone he could rely on— a family man, personally honest and conscientious, which was more than you could say for a lot of people who handled credit and money in Las Vegas. Every few months or so there would be reports of shortages at this hotel or that, and Milner heard through the grapevine that certain hotels owned by one man were being taken for big sums of money. All rumors, but rumors meant a great deal in Vegas. Where money was concerned, and big money, it was hard to control thievery. So he was happy with Chet, who, along with three unblinking TV cameras, kept an eye on the activity in the cashier's cage.

When Milner took over the operation of the El Capitan, his first priority was the junket programs, which were in shambles. Most of the Strip hotels had junkets—which entitled big players (or, as the term was commonly used, "qualified players") to fly to Vegas, stay in a room, eat meals and drink liquor, all for free. That was essentially what a junket was: a group of these qualified players who arrived on a plane to gamble and had all these benefits. Players who wanted to be included had to be recommended by other players or people in the gaming business. To show their good faith, these new players had to put up $3,000 in advance before flying out. Once the player was known and had a reputation as a legitimate gambler, he was given credit without the front money, but until he established his reputation, the front money had to be put up.

Before Milner became president, the junket program

in the El Capitan was nothing more than a flimsy excuse for a lot of free riders and deadbeats to fly to Vegas for nothing, and to take advantage of the hotel's free services. These players were known as D players. The El Capitan used a classification system that rated junket gamblers from A to D. The A players were the very best, those with unlimited credit, or credit exceeding $50,000 for each trip. B players were also very good credit risks and gave the casino a big play at the tables. The C group was border-line, and D players were at the bottom, never to be in-vited again on a junket.

Milner, upon taking control of the El Capitan, immedi-ately held meetings with the shift and pit bosses, telling them that it was essential for the future of the hotel that they watch the activities of the players coming out on these free trips. Most of the junket players didn't realize that all the floormen in the pit, as well as the boxmen, were reporting on their action to Chet Gardner, the credit manager, who would determine whether they should be invited on future junket trips. This was important to the El Capitan, for half the gaming profits came from the junket program.

"I have the records here on both the Chicago and New York junkets," said Chet. "I'll start with the Chicago one first. It's easier. Del Agelof runs a good program, and he brings in good players."

Milner nodded.

"There's still an awful lot of competition for the A players," Chet said, "and we can't compete on the same scale as the Grand or the Hilton or Caesars. But we get our share. A lot of players feel lost in these big hotels. I talk to them, they tell me. Here, they're catered to; they're known."

"That's my concept in a nutshell, Chet. We're smaller and we make up for it in friendliness. I've been keeping on the shift bosses' ass about that. I want them to be friendly to the players, to show the players that they're important to us."

"Well, it's working, Harry. I know it is. By the way, did you straighten out that thing with Mike English?"

"Temporarily, at least. You got the report, didn't you?"

"Yes. Fifteen G's credit for the two weeks. Harry, you know as well as I do, that isn't going to last him through this weekend. Not the way he plays."

"What can I do? I feel like the guy putting a finger in the dike. I'd like to control the bastard, but these guys, they're degenerates, and there's nothing you can do with them."

"They're all the same, Harry. They should see themselves the way we see them. All the same. There are those who are losing and want to get even, and those who are winning and want to make a killing. And in the long run, the losers lose more and the winners lose what they won and end up down the drain."

"Isn't that the truth? You think they'd know better. But then, we'd be out of business if they played like sane men."

"No lie," said Gardner. "Look at Mike English. He dropped a big bundle at craps, tried to make it up in baccarat today, and went for another bundle. I got the full report from the floor. He bet bank and lost, then switched to player and lost, went back and forth, the old whiplash principle. He just sat there, getting angrier and angrier, and couldn't buy a winning bet."

"I hope he shows up on the stage tonight. Jesus, what an unreliable bastard he is, and here we are, dependent on him. Like holding onto a tiger's tail. How much is he in to us for?"

"Twelve big ones. Three thousand more and his credit is exhausted."

"And the shit hits the fan," said Milner. "You know, Chet, you may think I'm crazy, but if it were up to me, I'd cancel the goddamn markers and let him play all he wants to. Make believe he's playing with Monopoly money. His lousy fifteen grand isn't going to make that much difference to us, but if he pulls out of the show, or doesn't show up, then we go down the tubes. The guy can generate a fortune for us. I'd let him play and just tear up the markers."

"Why don't we do that?"

"Huh? With Balofsky looking over our shoulders? Shit would *really* hit the fan then."

Gardner got up and went into the washroom. He took a Valium, then came back and sat down again. "Harry," he said, "if you think of it logically, aren't we really in the business of destroying people?"

Milner ground out his cigarette and leaned forward. "Chet, don't ever talk that way. What are you thinking of, that Farkas deal?"

"No, Harry, I swear, I wasn't thinking about Farkas."

"That was an accident. I did what I could. What else could I have done?"

"Harry, I swear to you, I wasn't thinking about him at all."

"All right. I'm just tired."

"To change the subject," said Gardner, "we've got a lot of wives and/or girlfriends on the New York junket."

"How do you know the difference?"

"Harry, I don't know the difference and don't care. I just put down if they came with a woman. So long as they pay $300 for her seat on the plane, they could bring a hippo for all I care."

"Some of these guys bring hippos."

"No lie. I was about to talk to you about the Grossmans from New York. Did you ever see Mrs. Grossman? She weighs close to two hundred fifty pounds, and every time they sit down in the steak house, they run up a $60 bill, at least."

"They're not eating in the gourmet room, are they?"

"No way. I completely agree with you about only A players being comped in the gourmet room. And the Grossmans, unless I'm mistaken, are just deadbeats, just D players."

"He had a higher rating last time, didn't he?"

"Yes, he did. The last credit report on him had him down as a B player, you know, a steady quarter player. He'd go for ten or fifteen markers a trip and that adds up. But, Harry, I got some reports from the floormen on Grossman. It seems he came here with another player, Ben Harding."

"This is on the New York junket?"

"Yes. Well, here's what they do. Harding goes to one end of the table and Grossman to the other. Harding bets fifty bucks pass and Grossman fifty bucks don't-pass, with the guy betting don't-pass throwing a couple of bucks on the 12, just in case. So they go back and forth, and they just about even out, and we get no real play from them. It looks like action, but it's nothing but bullshit."

"How'd you find this out?"

"From Perrino, one of the floormen. And I spoke to our man in the eye in the sky, John Holland, and he verified it. So we're stuck with two deadbeats."

"Didn't that bastard in New York, what's his name, check them out?"

"You mean Seymour Brass? He has his head up his ass half the time, Harry. He just went along with the old list."

"He should have checked them out."

"Well, to tell you the truth, these two couples have been coming here for a year now."

"This is definitely their last trip."

"What do you want me to do?"

"Chet, if this were the Dunes, they'd have to pay for their room and board, and the flight home. They'd be told they were deadbeats right up and down."

"You want me to speak to them . . . tell them this?"

"Hell, no, Chet. Don't put yourself on the line with deadbeats. Call in Brass and tell him the situation. Then let him tell the people that no more meals will be comped, nothing more will be comped. We'll take care of their flights home, but if they raise a big stink, then we'll tell them to pay for the airfare. I won't stand for this kind of crap. If a guy doesn't want to play, that's his business. Let him get one of these special deals to Vegas, and stay at the Stardust or somewhere. But I don't like the idea of them coming here and taking advantage of us."

"The Sawdust would be a good place for them."

"Yes," agreed Milner, "grind heaven. Or the Silver Nugget."

"Well," said Chet, "I better get back to my office. That covers the problems."

"Thanks. You're doing a great job, Chet. Keep it up."

"Got nothing better to do. Listen, Harry, I meant to ask you. Grace wanted to know if you wanted to drop by for some drinks tonight. Nothing special, but if you want to . . ."

"When?"

"Anytime you want."

"I may do that."

"Hear from Mary?"

"Yes, she'll probably be back at the beginning of the week."

"Well, see if you can make it tonight."

"OK. Thanks, Chet."

After the credit manager left, Milner went to the window and opened the curtains. The sun was still shining, and the swimming pool was still filled with floating fat bodies from the two junkets. He closed the drapes and went to the closet for his jacket. Time for that little trip with Moe Lewis to see the boys.

16

Milner pulled the Porsche up in front of the ranch house on East Oakey, near Eastern Avenue. It was a residential street, and the house looked like all the others on the block, with its burnt-out lawn and the white stones on its roof.

He quickly got out of the car and waited for Moe Lewis to struggle out of the passenger seat. They walked slowly to the front door, and Milner rang the bell. Chimes sounded. The door opened.

"Well, well, well," said Tiny Shapiro, his deep voice full of exuberance. "If it isn't my old friend, Harry. And Moe. Great seeing you both." He put his arms around the men and led them into the living room where Leon Balofsky, Sol Balofsky's nephew, was standing. Leon shook hands with Lewis and Milner.

"How about a drink, Harry?" Tiny asked.

"OK. That sounds good."

"Name your poison."

"You have any Scotch?"

"Sure we have Scotch. How do you want it?"

"On the rocks. With a little water."

"And you, Moe? I know you don't drink. How about a Coke, seven-up?"

"Seven-up."

"Coming right up." Tiny Shapiro was a big man; at one time he had weighed 260 pounds. He was six foot two, but illness had shrunk him down. His large frame was still there, but now the clothes hung on his body as if he were a scarecrow, and his skin was gray.

Milner was shocked by his appearance. Shapiro was Mr. B's right-hand man, but not for long, thought Milner. No wonder Balofsky was selling out; he was running out of men to watch over his interests.

The drinks were served and the men sat down. Tiny gave Moe a fresh cigar and he and Moe lit up, while Milner put a cigarette to his lips and lit it with the snap of a gold lighter. The smoke hung heavily in the air.

"So, Tiny," asked Milner, "what brings you to Vegas again?"

"Well, it's always a pleasure coming here. I always liked the town, Harry. There's no place like it, you gotta admit that."

"That I'll admit."

"No place like it. The last twenty-four-hour town in America. Yeah, no place like Vegas. And Harry, I can remember the old days, when I worked in the casinos with Moe. Moe, remember those old days?"

The casino manager grinned.

"Tell him about Bugsy," Shapiro urged Moe.

"You mean Mr. Benjamin Siegel," said Lewis. "No one called him Bugsy to his face. It was always Ben, not even Benny, just Ben. Yeah, the old days. You know something, Tiny, there aren't many old-timers around. This town is getting old. When did it all get started, around '45, '46? That's thirty years ago."

"Yeah," said Shapiro, "the old days. Tommy Hull and his Rancho Vegas, then Bugsy and the Flamingo. That was a crazy time. The builders robbed Bugsy blind when they put up the Flamingo. In those days you couldn't get any building supplies. It was right after the war, and he paid a fortune for what he could get. They'd deliver lumber to him in the afternoon, and steal it back at night and re-deliver it the next day. But Bugsy kept paying, because he wanted that hotel finished. He wanted it so bad. And he got it."

"And got his," said Moe.

"Yeah, what can you do? You can't fight the whole world, the way Bugsy tried. You can't just spit in everyone's face. I told Ben; I said, 'Ben, don't piss in the wind, that's what you're doing, pissing in the goddamn wind.' "

"And what did he say?" Leon Balofsky asked. He was about thirty, a different generation from the men sitting with him. He had dark hair, an olive complexion, a round face with large brown eyes.

"He told me to shut the fuck up, so I did. You couldn't argue with him. He was in his own world. I remember that room he had over the pool in the Flamingo, you remember that, Moe?"

"Yeah, he'd be shouting orders to everyone from there. He had this loudspeaker setup, and there would come his voice, blasting someone from his room, shouting at the top of his lungs. He scared the shit out of everybody. Or he'd come into the casino and push players around, telling them to go and play, not just stand around. You just couldn't do those kind of things, but there was nobody to tell him no. Till they finally got to him."

"Who did it?" Leon asked Moe.

"Leon, ask your uncle," said Lewis. "He knows better than me."

"Anyway, forget about Bugsy," said Shapiro. "Harry, you asked me why I came out to Vegas. I'll tell you. You know Mr. B wants to unload, and he has the buyer right now. A corporation from Cleveland in the food-franchise business. They're businessmen. We got to deal with them like businessmen, so I brought Leon here to check it all out. Mr. B wants to make them happy. He wants to have answers for all their questions."

"And their first question," said Leon Balofsky, "is why we don't have a 20 percent p.c. on the table games." He was referring to the house's profits or winning percentage.

"That's the long and short of it, Harry," said Shapiro. "The p.c. is low and sticks out like a sore thumb. Those guys are going to ask questions. They already know what to expect in the way of a drop and p.c. I mean, this town has a lot of this kind of businessman running things now. The whole town's legit, with some exceptions, but that's another story. Right now, they expect certain things. But you explain it, Leon, you're the accountant."

"All right, Harry, let's look at the figures." Leon took out a group of computer sheets from a briefcase and passed copies around.

"For our hotel," Leon said, "we got 650 rooms, right? OK, for this size hotel, we should have a drop of 6 million a month, and a hold percentage of 20 percent. That's a profit on twenty-one and craps of 1.2 million a month."

"That's the way I look at it," said Milner.

"Good, we're in agreement, right? Now, what we have is slightly more than 5 million for the drop, and a p.c. of 17 percent."

"It's closer to 18 percent," said Milner.

"The point is, whether it's 17 or 18, it's not 20 percent. That means," said the accountant, "that 2 or 3 percent is going somewheres. It's not going to us in profits; it's disappearing somewheres."

Milner put on his gold-rimmed reading glasses and looked at figures he was quite familiar with. The records on the sheets went back a year, to the time he first took over, when the El Capitan was nearly bankrupt. The drop figures, representing the gross business done at the craps and blackjack tables, were just only $3 million then.

"What about the drop, Leon?" asked Milner. "No comment about how that's been moving up?"

"It's great," said Leon, "and don't think, Harry, that Mr. B doesn't appreciate the job you've done, but the hold is down for the last two months. Even when we had half this drop, we had a hold of 20 percent. Harry, 20 percent is a figure I'm pulling out of my hat. That's the expected profit, right?"

"That's right."

"You know," said the accountant, "gambling is the kind of business that's all numbers, all percentages. Now, on the Strip, a hotel like ours makes close to a million for each craps table, right? 950 thou or thereabouts. We take in over a million on the baccarat. We take in about 950 thou for the slots. These are all basic figures. And when they don't jell, when we don't take in this kind of profit, we have to see what's happening, right?"

"You're giving me figures we don't take in. We don't make that kind of money on our craps operation."

"Well, we know why," said Leon. "It's because we don't have the expected drop. But the p.c., the hold, that should be constant, no matter what the drop. You take in $10 in the drop box, you should make a $2 profit. You take in a million, there should be $200,000 profit. But not less. When we lose three points on our hold, it's going somewhere else."

"Not necessarily," said Milner. "We may be having a bad run. That happens."

"Anything can happen," chimed in Moe.

"I don't believe in luck," said Leon. "And I don't think you do either, Harry. Percentages are percentages."

"As I said, not necessarily," Milner countered. "Some hotels aren't making any profit at all, and the p.c. in those places is nowhere near 20 percent."

"Sure," said Leon. "When those hotels got a crazy owner nobody can find, that happens. But there are other hotels, Harry, and my uncle can tell you about them, where the hold was low, and some sons of bitches were grabbing checks off the tables, left and right. When the owners found out about them, they straightened that situation out fast."

"So what you're saying," Moe said, "is that we're being taken. Cheated."

"The figures don't lie," said Leon.

"I run a tight casino."

"You can't be everywhere at once."

"Hey, you telling me I don't know my business?" Moe said, waving his cigar angrily.

"I'm not telling you that, you know that, Moe. I'm just saying these thieves, they have ways of taking a casino. I know you know your business, Moe, but the figures tell us that money is missing."

"Or it could be a bad run," Moe said. "When Caesars first got Sinatra to perform, they had their biggest drop ever. I saw the figures. But they weren't making money at the tables. They lost money the first week he was in their showroom."

"And what about the second week?" asked Leon. "They made it up the second week, in spades. If they had a loss the second week, then something would have been wrong. Now, in the El Capitan, we're not talking about one week. We're talking about two months. So something's wrong. And Mr. B feels that way also. He's disturbed about it, and wants to know how he's going to explain it away."

There was silence in the room.

"Another drink, Harry?" Shapiro asked.

"OK. Thanks."

There was a pause as the drink was poured and cigars and cigarettes were relit. The tension lessened. Leon was still taut and disturbed.

"All right," said Milner, the drink warming his guts. "Leon, what does Mr. B want?"

"He wants you to find where the money is going. In two

areas. The blackjack pit on the swing shift. And craps 3 on all the shifts."

"Craps 3 has lost some money because of one roller," said Milner. "And I know the hold is low on that table, but only the last couple of weeks." He lit another cigarette. "We've already changed the crews twice. I'm sure it's a temporary thing. Nothing's going on there. It's just been a bad table for us."

"What about the blackjack situation?"

"That's something else," said Milner. "We've increased our surveillance there. If there's something wrong, we'll find it."

"Find it," said Shapiro, "and then our problem is solved."

"We'll find it. We'll really check everything out, double-check from the tables to the counting room."

"Now you're talking my language," said Leon.

"Good." Milner finished his second drink.

"Then that's settled," said Shapiro. "You find out what's wrong . . ."

"If anything's wrong," said Harry.

"Yes, of course, if anything's wrong. If nothing's wrong, good also. We just want answers to these businessmen's questions."

"It'll be done," said Milner.

"Fine, wonderful," said Shapiro.

The men stood up and walked toward the front door. Milner drew Shapiro aside. "Tiny, what's this I hear about Augie Panetta being in town?"

"Who told you that?"

"That's what I heard."

"No comment."

"Why is he here?"

"Harry, don't worry your head off about our business, OK? Don't worry. Like I told you, you run your end of things and we'll run our end. But, Harry, if you find something wrong, I want to know right away."

"And Augie will take care of it?"

Shapiro smiled. "Harry, what are you saying? I told you, don't worry about such things. Great seeing you again. And keep in touch. I'll be here all week."

He gave Milner a bearhug, and the hotel president left the house.

17

At seven in the morning, after a few hours' sleep, Steinberg returned to the El Capitan and rang Thornton's room. There was no answer. He went up to the room and knocked on the door; still no response. Then he cruised the casino and the grounds of the hotel, but if Thornton was around, he was making himself scarce. Steinberg returned at nine and then at ten-thirty, each time going through the same routine.

On his last visit, he went to the room clerk and asked if Thornton was still a guest at the hotel.

"Yes, sir," said the clerk. "He's paid up through Sunday, and he hasn't checked out yet."

"He might have just taken off. Is there any way his room could be checked?" Steinberg asked.

"I'm afraid not."

Steinberg slipped $5 into the clerk's hand. "It's important that I know whether or not he's occupying the room. Maybe you can call one of the cleaning women and have her check the room. Maybe I could check it with her."

"I'll call up, but you can't go into a guest's room. She'll look in."

"OK, I'll settle for that."

Steinberg waited while the clerk called up to the third floor. A few minutes later, the woman called back and said the room was still occupied, but no one was in it. "The clothes and toilet articles are still there," the clerk told him.

"That's what I wanted to know. What's your name?"

"Paul."

"Paul, I'm Don Steinberg. You can do me a big favor. I'll leave my number with you. If Thornton returns to the hotel, give me a ring at this number. And if there's no answer, try this other number and leave a message." He gave the clerk Diane's phone number. "If you do that," Steinberg said, "there'll be something nice in it for you."

"This isn't going to get me in any trouble, is it?"

"No way. I won't mention it to anyone. The bum owes me money and I want to collect it before he skips town. I live in Vegas myself."

"All right, I'll see what I can do."

"Thanks a million."

Steinberg had been in his apartment since eleven that morning and no call came from Paul at the El Capitan. It was early afternoon and he was dozing off when the phone rang. It was Diane.

"What's happening, baby?" she asked.

"Nothing much."

"Did I wake you?"

"Yes. That's OK."

"Listen, can I come over? I just have to get out of this place; it's such a mess, and I called and got a cleaning woman over and I can't stand the racket. She's vacuuming now."

"Sure, come on over."

Diane was there in fifteen minutes. She was wearing tight jeans and an embroidered white T-shirt.

She kicked off her sandals and sat heavily on the couch.

"You want a drink?" he asked.

"I could use one. What've you got?"

"I don't know." He opened the cupboards above the kitchen sink. "Got some Wild Turkey. How about that and some ice?"

She nodded and lit a cigarette. "You know, in all the time I know you, I've never been to your place. Mind if I look around, Don?"

"Go ahead."

She went into the bathroom. Don heard the water flush, then he saw her in his bedroom, looking over the things he had on his dresser.

"Who's this a picture of?" she asked, from the bedroom.

"What?"

Diane brought out a picture, framed in a silver case. It was of a young woman, smiling slightly, her eyes warm and bright.

"That was my wife."

"Oh." Diane studied the picture. "She's beautiful. What's her name?"

"Her name was Paula. She died about a year ago."

Diane put down the picture carefully on the coffee table.

"I know you don't want to talk about it," she said, taking the drink he offered her. She watched him down about half his own drink, noting how exhausted he looked. His eyes were bloodshot and his face was pale. She stared at him as he looked at the picture, picking it up tentatively, then putting it down, turning it so that he no longer could see the face.

"What the hell," he said, finishing his drink. He got up and poured another and sat down again. "She was a beautiful person," he said. "Beautiful. Diane, she was the only one in my life who ever made me happy. Everyone else fucked me over: my father, my stepmother, the courts, the army, everyone. Then I met Paula and she changed my life. You know what I mean . . . when I was with her, my heart was full of songs . . . I was overflowing all the time. I was filled with happiness. With joy."

Diane blew out some smoke and continued to look at Steinberg's face. His eyes were clouded over. She wanted to say something to comfort him, but she didn't want to interrupt him, and she didn't know what to say.

"She got pregnant, and there were complications. The fucking doctor told us she needed a hysterectomy, only it wasn't so simple. The fucking butcher got through with her, and they took her to the morgue."

He finished the drink. "I paid for the hospital, everything. It wiped me out. Then the fucker sent me his bill. I called him up and told him I'd kill him if he sent me another bill."

"Did you have any kids?" Diane asked.

"No. That was our first. It was going to be a little girl. Ah, I don't even know why I'm talking about this." He got up and poured another drink and drank it down. "I'm so fucking tired. I'm tired, Diane. I played with that mother, Thornton, and the bastard ran off with my share of the winnings. He owed me about six or seven big ones and he ran out of the Hilton without giving me my share."

"He did that?"

"Yeah. I've been at the El Capitan all morning looking for him. He's laying low, hiding out somewhere, but I'll find him."

Diane could see the rage in Don's face, and the tears in his eyes. She was embarrassed because of his tears. He'd never been like this before. She got up and went over to him, putting her arms around him. "Baby, baby," she said, "come on in the other room. Let me hold you."

"No . . ." He had turned his face away, but he stood up and let her guide him into the bedroom. She brought him gently down onto the bed.

"Now, Don, you relax. Let me put on some music." She

turned on the radio, and they lay in the darkened room, her arms around him. After a while he seemed to calm down.

"Is that why you came to Vegas?" she asked. "Because of what happened?"

He nodded.

"Why didn't you ever tell me? You could have told me. I'm your friend."

"I don't know."

"You want to smoke a joint with me?" she asked.

"No."

"OK, that's cool." She lit another cigarette, and they lay in silence, listening to the music, to their own minds beating.

Steinberg closed his eyes, feeling himself drifting to sleep. He opened them to see Diane standing by the bed. She had taken off her clothes.

"Take off your things," she said softly. He tried to move.

"Here," she said, "I'll help you. Here, let me help you."

He sat up, and she took off his shirt. Then he stood up and she took down his pants, then his underclothes. She slid off the covers of the bed and pulled him down onto the sheets with her. Then she noticed a jagged inch-wide scar that ran across his upper back to the middle of his right chest. She touched it lightly with the tips of her right fingers.

"Does it hurt?"

"No."

"You get that in Vietnam?"

"Yes."

"You sure it doesn't hurt when I do this?"

"Yes."

"And here, does it hurt here?"

"No, it's just scar tissue now."

"Poor baby."

"Shit," he said, "stop feeling sorry for me."

"I didn't mean it that way, honestly." She rubbed her hands over his torso, feeling how tight his body was, how wiry and muscular. She moved her hands down to his thighs.

"Does it feel good?" she asked.

"Yes."

"It's getting you excited, isn't it?"

"Yes, but I'm so beat, Diane."

"You take it easy. Just take it easy, baby. Baby, just take it easy."

She moved away and, still stroking him, sat on him, straddling his body, pushing him into her. When he entered, she closed her eyes tightly, taking a deep breath. "Oh, baby, oh, baby," she said. She could feel how hot her face was and looked down at Steinberg's face. His eyes were closed, and his lips were pressed together. "Oh, baby, baby, come to me," she said.

But he couldn't come that way, and Diane could feel him straining, feel his thighs moving urgently. At the same time, she felt her whole body seem to swell, felt the rush within her, felt her own shaking, but Don lay there, his lips pressed together, his torso straining, his buttocks off the mattress, rising in a final effort, but still he couldn't come.

She felt a strong orgasm overwhelm her body, bursting within her, and she let it consume her completely. And then she wanted more. She got off him and put her hands around his prick, feeling its heat, its smoothness all wet with her body fluid, and she stroked him, running her hands down inside his legs, stroking his thighs and then returning to his prick, and then she bent over and began to kiss his chest, his abdomen, feeling how sweaty he was, smelling her own odors on his skin, moving her mouth down past his pubic hair, finally taking his prick into her mouth.

Again she could feel him straining, feel his movement, feel his body seeking the relief, and she moved her head up and down, wiggling her tongue, her mouth filled with him, pausing at times to take a deep breath. He choked her with his size, but she was beyond any discomfort and wanted him so badly, wanted to feel his manhood in her mouth, feel the spurt and know that she had finally satisfied him. But still he couldn't come. Finally, she moved away from his thighs, moving her head back up to his chest.

"Is everything all right, baby?" she asked.

"Yes. I'm sorry . . . it's just that . . ."

"You don't have to explain . . . I understand," she said.

Don put a hand on her head and stroked her long silken hair, and she brushed her lips against his chest, feeling how hard it was.

"Baby, you want me to get on you again?" she asked.

"You don't have to . . ." he whispered.

"No, don't say that. It's not having to or not. I want to. I want you to come in me, I want to feel all of you."

And once more, without waiting for his reply, she was sitting on him, fitting him into her, and she moved slowly, her eyes closed, feeling his response, feeling that he was now going to let it all out.

Her body grew hot and sweaty, and waves of feeling overcame her. She could feel it start in her knees and then she was shaking all over, her whole body on the verge of collapse, and suddenly he was coming also, filling her up, and she grasped his thighs tightly with her hands.

"Oh, come to me, baby, that's it, come," she said in a hoarse whisper.

It was all over, but for a while she couldn't stop shaking.

Then she got off him, her whole body weak, moving herself alongside him, lying next to him, feeling his body heaving.

She put her arms around him, and with one hand she felt for the scar. She touched it and pressed him closer to her. She could feel his breathing change, feel him drift off to sleep.

Diane stayed awake in the dark bedroom, hearing the soft music and the whir of the air-conditioner. She wished she could sleep too, but all she could do was hold him and look down at his sleeping face.

18

The slots manager's office was to one side of the casino, behind a thick unmarked door. When Milner got there, Karl Derringer, the manager, opened it and let him in.

One of the security guards was standing over a thin young man who wore a dirty T-shirt, patched-up jeans, and dusty Wellington boots. That's the first thing Milner noticed, how dusty the boots were, as if he had been tramping all day in the desert.

"We just caught him, Mr. Milner," said Derringer, going to his desk and returning with a spoon and wire in his hamlike hands. "He tried the old trick with the machines. John Holland called down from the eye in the sky and we caught him."

"Was he working alone?"

"Holland says there was a young girl nearby, a blond, but she got out of there before we could catch her. Bill here says he knows who she is."

Bill Foster was the security guard. "I don't know her name or anything," he said, "but I've chased her out of here a couple of times. She's just a cheap hooker."

"Did we ever bust her?"

"No, but I wouldn't be surprised if she was busted a couple of times. Those free-lancers generally are."

Milner turned his attention back to the prisoner. He had a thin, pinched face, with a prominent nose and sallow cheeks, and looked no older than twenty-two or twenty-three. His long hair was matted and dusty, too.

"What's your name?" he asked the young man, who was sitting slumped in a chair, his hands cuffed in front of him. The prisoner didn't even look up at Milner. "I asked you, what's your name?" There was no response.

"We have his wallet here," said Derringer. "According to it, his name is John Egert, and he comes from Taos, New Mexico."

"You live in Taos, John?" Milner asked. The young man still didn't look up.

"Hey," said Milner, his voice rising slightly, "I'm talking to you."

The young man finally looked him in the eye. "You got no right. I want these cuffs off."

"We have no right to do what?"

"You can't hold me."

"No? Why not? There's a law that says we can. If we catch you in the act of committing a crime, we can detain you. And trying to cheat the slots is a bad crime in this state."

"I wasn't cheating nobody, nobody."

"Did you see him?" he asked Bill.

"Yes, sir. When I got the call from John Holland, I went over to the slots and there he was, with the spoon stuck down in the throat of the machine and he was trying to wire the machine."

"You definitely saw him?"

"Yes, sir. And John saw him too."

"Well," said Milner, "we have witnesses."

"I want these cuffs off."

"No way, John. First, I want to ask you some questions. Is this your spoon and wire?

"No."

"No?"

"Never saw them before."

"What were you doing by the slots?"

"I lost a nickel in one of your fucking machines and it wouldn't come out, so I hit the machine with my hand and this ape grabs me."

"Bill?"

"No sir, Mr. Milner. He was trying to wire the machine. I saw it with my own eyes."

"He's a fucking liar."

"John, you keep this up, and the next thing you know, you'll be doing time up in Carson City, and believe me, that jail is a bitch. I'm asking you to cooperate." He turned to Derringer. "Was anything lost?"

"No, Mr. Milner. The Bally machines have been rigged so that the spoon-and-wire trick doesn't work anymore. He was wasting his time."

"Well," said Milner to the prisoner, "we lost nothing. Now, we want to know about the woman with you. Who was she?"

"No one was with me."

"Come on. If you don't tell us, we'll simply turn you over to the sheriff. I'm giving you a last chance."

"You got no right."

"He must have learned the spoon trick from a former con," said Derringer. "It went out years ago."

"Where are you staying in Vegas?" Milner asked Egert.

"You got no right. Get these fucking cuffs off me."

"All right," said Milner. "Bill, take him to your office and call the sheriff. There's no point in talking to him anymore."

"OK, let's go," the security guard told the prisoner, who tried to stay in his chair. He was shoved to his feet and prodded out the door. Milner watched all of this, shaking his head. He had meant what he said. If the boy had co-operated, they'd have taken his picture, found his accomplice, and taken hers too, and made sure they were thrown out of Vegas. Now it would be in the hands of the law, out of his department.

"That punk," said Derringer. "I'd like to have had him in here alone for thirty minutes. After I got through with him, that kid would never go near slots again in his life." Derringer slammed one fist into the palm of his other hand. "They try everything. They used hair spray for awhile, diamond drills, everything. This punk didn't even know what he was doing. He couldn't spoon the machine and he was using the wire wrong. They used to 'shim' the Ballys by sticking the wire in and holding one reel in place. They can't do that on our machines now."

"I guess you've seen everything."

"Mr. Milner, not everything, but by the time I get finished here, I'll have seen everything. They come up with new gimmicks every day of the week. They used to have the 'handle-slammers,' but we stopped them. Up there," he said, as he pointed to a row of photographs of slots cheats above his desk, "that couple in the first row, they were caught downtown handle-slamming. They got ahold of some old machines and would slam the handle backwards while the reels were moving. But they got caught fast."

Derringer pointed to another photograph. "And that guy, he taught the rhythm method. He'd pick out a machine and keep working it till he could line up the right symbols. That bastard actually taught the method, got paid, had pupils. Can you imagine that? And some of these cheats still use it, especially on old machines with worn parts. We're always watching out for them."

"We haven't been hurt by cheats, have we, Karl?"

"No, Mr. Milner, we keep a good lookout. I'll tell you something. I'm still thinking of that punk in here a few minutes ago. In the old days, when we caught one of them . . . he didn't get off so easy. Before we turned him over to the law, we'd work on him first. Generally, by the time the sheriff got him, he had broken a couple of fingers on his hand and maybe both his hands. One time, we caught this punk and we took him out on the desert and left him there, kicking his ass in the direction of Salt Lake City. We let him shift for himself. He probably lasted six hours in that sun."

Milner lit a cigarette and listened. Derringer had been in the El Capitan since it opened. He knew his business and kept the machines functioning, and that was important. But Derringer was a relic from the old days, just looking for revenge on the cheats, for a good workout.

Milner left the slots manager's office and stood in the slots area, watching the early-afternoon players. Nearby a group of women were happily pulling the metal arms, looking for that jackpot. Each machine was numbered and each was checked by computer, to show its cumulative profits by day, week, month, and year. If the tally was off from the expected norm, the machine was immediately examined for signs of tampering.

The slots in the El Capitan were average in payoffs, giving the casino somewhere around 16 percent in profits. The machines in Vegas averaged between 6 to 20 percent profitability for the house. The 6 percent machines were known as "loose" ones, and many of the casinos continually advertised their "loose" machines. The El Capitan, unlike the downtown casinos, didn't cater to slots players, which was just as well, as far as Milner was concerned. He didn't like the idea of the casino turning into a circus, with bells ringing and lights flashing every time someone won $5 worth of nickels.

The El Capitan featured two basic kinds of slots—those that made straight payoffs and those that paid progressive or increasing jackpots. But the machines were all set, figured out mathematically, and whether a big jackpot was hit or the coins dribbled out in many small payoffs, the machines would make their percentages for the El Capitan. The profits amounted to almost a million dollars a year.

There were three reels on practically all the machines, and each reel held twenty symbols. The possibility of a slot machine running through all the possible combinations of symbols before repeating was reduced to a formula, which all the slots people knew by heart—20^3. It meant 20 times 20 times 20, or 8,000 combinations. For a casino to insure its profit, the slots mechanic set the machine to have a certain number of coins paid out in the course of those 8,000 pulls. If 6,400 coins were paid out, then 1,600 were retained for a profit percentage of 20 percent, and so on.

Milner knew that a "slot mix" was important; that is, a setup in which some slots would pay more than others, and thus attract more business to the casino. The El Capitan was set up in such a way so that the crowds waiting to get into the showroom were forced to line up along the banks of machines, and Milner took advantage of this fact to have those machines closer to the aisles pay the most frequent jackpots. By doing this, the tourists and first-time visitors, playing the machines near the aisle at random, were impressed with the loose machines and invariably returned later, after the show, to try their luck at other slots. Since the other machines were tight, eventually they'd give back the profits. And while the women played these machines, the men would drift over and play the table games.

Milner also knew that slots were generally played two at a time, and so they were adjusted so that every other machine was loose. What the player got on one machine, he or she generally gave back on the other.

No matter how tight the machines were, no matter how much profit they made for the casino, there was something inherently exciting about them, something that held the players who pulled the metal arms by the hour. A woman could get more of a thrill from twenty nickels, fresh and hot from the bowels of a slots, than a craps shooter could get from making his point and a thousand dollars.

It was madness, thought Milner, and it was to him a symbol of what gambling seemed to be all about. It was the desire to enter the unknown, untested world, the world in which no one knew what was going to happen next. In life, in work, day by day, the average person knew roughly what his future would be. Tomorrow would be like today, and next week like tomorrow. But here, in the casino, the next pull of the lever, the next roll of the dice, the next card drawn in that suspended world of gaming, anything could happen. To find out what was coming up next meant to play, and to gamble meant to pay for the privilege.

19

Sitting in Milner's office was Tom Durham, the publicity director of the El Capitan, his shaggy red hair like an unkempt carpet.

"Harry, I hate to bother you now, but I wanted to show you the figures from the showroom."

Milner sat down wearily and lit a cigarette.

"Look, if you're not in the mood, we'll go over them some other time."

"Let's look at them now."

Durham spread out the sheets that were distributed daily by all the hotels, showing the attendance at each showroom in Las Vegas. It was one of the few ways the hotels accommodated each other.

"We've sold out every night that English has been on, both midnight and dinner shows, with the exception of the Thursday midnight show."

"It's hard to believe the hold that asshole has on the public."

"I've seen a couple of the shows, Harry. Have you been to any of them?"

"No. And if you ask if I'm going, the answer is also no."

Durham smiled. "It's amazing," he continued, "the way this guy gets out on the stage and turns into a little boy. The bastard's over forty by now, but on that stage you see a helpless kid singing his heart out, and the women love it, they just love it. You could see the handkerchiefs come out, tears running down their faces."

"Yes," said Milner, "I can see it all, the keno napkins from the coffee shop being used to wipe off the wet mascara."

"You know, Harry, you're getting cynical in your old age."

"God help me if I get cynical in this job. God help me then."

Durham shook his head. "The Lido keeps selling out," he said, looking at the showroom figures. "If the Stardust has one thing going for it, it's that show. They may have a grind operation, but they have the Lido. It's been selling out for years."

"It's a good show," said Milner. He looked over the Hilton figures, which weren't sellouts. "You know, Tom, the Hilton could be doing better. If they had Presley on this week, God damn, the figures would knock your eyes out. He's supposed to be getting 175 big ones a week."

"And he's underpaid," said Durham, "or so I hear. I hear he could get 250 a week, and the Hilton would still do well with his show."

"Those numbers; they're crazy, and getting crazier all the time. But what can you do? There are so few acts that can fill a main showroom, and everyone's scrambling for them."

"And you know the taste of Vegas," said Durham. "I remember Woody Allen's show at the Riviera. I think the guy is great, but he bombed out the place. There was no one in the showroom."

"He's the wrong show for Vegas. You know another one that bombed? Sid Caesar at the Frontier. That was years ago, I think it was '67 or '68, and I swear, Tom, I was in the showroom with a few friends and there were more people on stage than in the audience."

He inhaled and slowly blew out smoke. "We had some bombs ourselves, I guess," he said. "That goddamn show we had last week. I don't even want to think about it. That broad should go back to making commercials again."

"She's too old even for that."

"I have a bad taste in my mouth from that show. We were scraping the barrel then, but we won't make that mistake again. The last time I listen to Vincente. Some entertainment director! That guy's mind is gone."

"Well, now we have a live one. Mike English, the great one himself."

"And what do we pay him, twenty-five G's a week? He's a steal. We could pay him sixty a week and do well."

"Don't let him hear it."

"He knows it. He's no fool and neither is his manager. Something is going to happen. You just wait and see."

"I believe you. We had dealings with Arnold Goldstein at the old place, you remember?"

"Don't remind me."

The phone rang. It was the craps pitboss, Al Beatty.

"What's up?" Milner asked.

"Mike English just tapped out at the craps table and he's screaming bloody murder. He wants more credit."

"Tell him no more credit. Get rid of him."

Milner hung up the phone.

"Shit," he said to Durham. "English tapped out at the tables."

"What do you think he's going to do?"

"My feeling, my gut feeling? My feeling is that he's going to be crashing through this door in about five minutes. We have five minutes to protect ourselves from mayhem. Five minutes."

"What are you going to do?"

Milner shrugged, picked up his private phone and dialed Shapiro's number. Shapiro was called to the phone and his hoarse voice came on. "Yeah, Harry?"

"Tiny, we're going to have a problem here with Mike English. He's tapped out, and if he can't play any more at the tables, he's going to take a powder. I'm sure of it."

"He can't do that. We got a contract with him, don't we?"

"He'll tell me to shove it up my ass."

"I'll get back to you, Harry," said Shapiro and hung up.

"You think you ought to call Mr. B?" Durham asked Milner.

"No, Tiny's handling his business here. He's probably calling him."

Milner let a cigarette and waited. He didn't have to wait long. A few minutes later, there was a knock on his door. It was Chet Gardner.

"Harry, I have Mike English outside. I don't know how to handle him."

"Send him in here."

"You sure you want to see him?"

"Don't worry, just send him in here."

The singer entered, his face a mottled pink, his eyes wild and bloodshot, his hair in disarray, his look one of a wild man.

"That son of a bitch," he said, referring to Chet with his thumb. "He tells me I can't play anymore. And that son of a bitch in the casino, that pitboss of yours—who the fuck is he?—he thinks he's going to humiliate me in front of a bunch of fucking players."

"Now, take it easy, Mike. Sit down."

"Get these fucks out of here, Harry. I want to talk to you alone."

"These are my men," Milner said calmly, thinking of the sold-out show tonight—all their profits dependent on this creep.

"I don't care who the fuck they are. I want them out."

"Don't tell me to throw my men out of my office."

"What is this bullshit? I'm getting the fuck out of here." The singer glared at Harry and turned on his heels and was gone.

"What now?" asked Durham.

Milner took a deep breath. "He's either going to pack up and leave or come to his senses and see me again. The question is," said Milner, grinding out his cigarette, "whether he wants more action at the tables. That's the one hold we have on him. The contract is just a worthless piece of paper."

"I hope you're right," said Tom.

The phone rang. It was Shapiro. Milner told him what English had done.

"Where is he now?"

"Tiny, I don't know. Could be in his room, anyplace."

"Harry, see if you can find him, do me a favor."

"I'll send some men around to find him. He's probably in his room."

"Find him. As soon as you can, Harry."

"OK."

"And call me the minute you do," Tiny Shapiro said.

20

The meeting was held in Mike English's rooms on the penthouse floor overlooking the tennis courts. Shapiro, Milner, and Arnold Goldstein were there. Goldstein had just flown in from LA for the conference.

"I just won't put up with this bullshit," said the singer. "No more bullshit."

"Now, take it easy, Mike," said his manager.

Mike snorted and pouted and got up and paced around the room like a cat, almost snarling.

"Sit down, Mike," said Shapiro. "Sit down and let's talk. What's the problem anyway? You want to play, right? That's what this whole problem is about."

English fell back into the overstuffed chair facing the sofa on which Milner and Shapiro sat. Goldstein, a small man with fuzzy blondish hair that looked dyed, was sitting next to English on another chair.

"That's right," said English. "That's exactly right. I want to play when I feel like and when I want to. I don't want to be humiliated the way I was by these bastards." He pointed to Milner. "Harry, I never expected it of you. I thought you were my friend. But to humiliate me like that! You and that pitboss."

"Look, I didn't humiliate you. What did you want me to do? You used up your credit. You know what your credit line was. When you used it up, what did you want me to do, run out on the floor and empty my own pockets?"

"See?" he asked his manager. "See the way he talks to me? You see that?"

Milner blew out some smoke. "Jesus Christ, Mike, you're a big boy now. Act like a man, will you? No one's trying to make you look bad. We're here to straighten this thing out."

"That's right," said Goldstein. "Now, take it easy. It was Harry who recommended you for the job in the first place, remember that?"

"No, he doesn't remember that," said Milner. "He only remembers what he wants to remember. He has a convenient memory." Milner could feel his voice rising. *Take it easy,* he told himself, *take it easy.* But all afternoon he had been wrung out by the singer's situation, calling LA to get Goldstein here, calling back and forth with Shapiro. The punk had worn him out. He could feel his nerves at their breaking point. *I need a rest,* he told himself, *I need to get away from this madhouse.*

"You're in to us for fifteen G's right now," Shapiro said. "With taxes and all, I figure you're tapped out for the two weeks now, including salary."

"Let my manager worry about the taxes," English told Shapiro.

"We all have to worry now," said Shapiro. "All right, Mike, you want some kind of deal? What do you want?"

"I've spoken to Mike," said Goldstein, "and I've seen the showroom figures. You're selling out every show. You have my boy here at bargain prices. You couldn't get anyone else for twenty-five G's a week to sell out a main showroom."

"That's right," said Milner, "but a deal's a deal. We'll work something out for the next appearances, but we have a signed contract for this one."

"The point is," continued Goldstein, "you could pay Mike fifty G's a week and still have a bargain. Right now

147

you have a super bargain. You just can't sell out a show-room for that kind of money. Look what the Dunes spends on Casino de Paris, or the MGM or the Stardust on their shows. It costs them millions and here you got one performer packing them in. And you're paying him pennies."

The room was silent for a couple of minutes.

"What are you telling us?" Milner asked.

"Let's renegotiate the contract right now. It's now six, five to six. By the time he does his show at eight, I want a new deal for Mike."

"And if you don't get one?" Shapiro asked.

"I don't know. It's up to Mike then."

"I take the next plane out of this town. I swear to you, that's what I do."

"Hey, c'mon," said Shapiro. "You do that, and you're washed up in Vegas. And a lot of other places. You're dealing with us, Mike. You know who we are?"

"Don't threaten him," said Goldstein.

"I'm not threatening him, I'm telling him. Mike English or no Mike English. You're not that big, Mike, that you can't be brought down to size."

"I told you, don't threaten him."

"Hey, Arnold, who you speaking to, huh?" Shapiro's gray face had turned white, and his dark brown eyes stood out like berries.

"All right, I'm sorry, Tiny. I'm sorry. All right? But all I'm asking is that we talk business. It's business, that's all. Isn't it, Harry?"

Milner said nothing.

"Harry and I want to talk together," said Shapiro. "You two take a walk for a while."

"Hey, Tiny, these are my rooms," said the singer.

"Your rooms? I could throw you out of here in a minute, out of these rooms. You're here as my guest." Shapiro had turned ultra-gray again. His voice shook as he spoke.

"Come on, Mike, we'll go down and walk around the tennis courts," said Goldstein.

"I'm not walking on any fucking tennis courts. We'll go into the bedroom, but we're not leaving these rooms."

"Go into the bedroom then," said Shapiro. He was panting for breath.

Harry poured Tiny a drink of Canadian Club and watched Shapiro drink it, holding onto the glass with shaking fingers.

"That little prick," said Shapiro, when he could talk again. "I should take the little fuck and destroy him by myself."

"He'll destroy himself with his playing."

"That prick." Shapiro poured himself another whiskey and drank it down, then wiped his mouth with the back of his right hand. "Harry, Harry, what do you think?"

"What can I say, Tiny? This is Friday . . . In a couple of hours, the show is supposed to go on. There are lines extending into the street for this dinner show. If he quits, there goes our weekend. It's over, gone."

"We could get someone else."

"Who? And on an hour's notice? No way, Tiny. And whoever we get, it's going to cost at least fifty G's for the week."

"I don't want to give in to him. I never did to any prick like that."

"We'll compromise. Tiny, if it were any other time, I'd say you were right. Don't give in. But we have the buyers coming Sunday. This will be the deathblow to selling the hotel. It'll wreck the whole deal."

Shapiro sat heavily in the chair and breathed deeply.

"Look," said Milner. "We'll tear up the fucking contract. It's worth nothing anyway. We'll offer him thirty-five G's a week for these two weeks. That'll give him twenty more to play with. In any case he'll end up giving it all back to us on the tables."

"You're talking sense, Harry. I got to admit it. It's just the prick. I can't stand him."

"He's a jerk, Tiny. You can't deal with jerks."

"He thinks because I'm old, I can't put him into the ground still."

"Fuck him, Tiny. We're in a bad spot now. Our time will come."

"All right, tell them to come in."

Goldstein and English listened to Milner's offer with sullen faces. Then Goldstein shook his head.

"It's no good. He deserves even more than fifty, which was what I wanted for him. We should shoot for sixty a week."

"No way," said Milner. "Arnold, be reasonable. We're giving you ten more each week, ten more than we have to. And after this gig, he gets fifty big ones for any week he appears."

"No."

"Look," said Milner, "the new contract will obligate Mike to appear three more times in the coming year at fifty G's a week. After that, you can make your own deal."

Goldstein didn't answer.

"Mike," said Shapiro, "you want to play, don't you? You just got yourself twenty grand to play with. And a big raise for the remaining shows you'll put on. What the hell else do you want?"

Mike asked to speak to his manager. They went into the bedroom.

"What do you think?" the singer asked his manager.

"I think we've gone far enough, Mike. I think we should take what they offer."

"You can get more, Arnold. They're up against it this weekend. They got an hour till the show."

"Sure we can get more, if I put them to the wall. But you don't want to put Tiny Shapiro to that wall, Mike. He's no guy you can push around. He may be sick but he's still dangerous."

English pondered that.

"Listen," said Goldstein, "the word is that they're selling out anyway. There'll be a new group taking over soon, a corporation. We can deal with them later. We can always renegotiate with the new people."

"You think so?"

"I know so. And Mike, these businessmen aren't guys like Shapiro and Balofsky." The manager spoke rapidly and now paused and came up close to his client, whispering. "I'll tell you one other thing I heard. Augie Panetta's in town."

"What?"

"So let's be cool. We made our play. You got your extra twenty grand and a good deal for the coming year. Let's cool it now. Let's be able to sleep nights."

"OK."

"But I'm telling you this, Mike, and it's between me and you. Don't leave your fucking money at the tables here. Stop playing or you'll wind up where you were before."

"Hey, Arnold, if I want your advice about my personal life, I'll ask for it, OK?"

"This is not personal, this is money."

"To me it's personal."

The manager shrugged.

"You hear from Rhonda?" Mike asked.

"Yeah, I saw her the other day. She misses you."

"I thought she'd come out to see my show," said English. "She said she might come, but she never showed."

Goldstein shrugged. *If I wasn't fucking her,* he said silently, *she'd be here to see you, asshole.*

They opened the door to the living room and went back to finish the deal with Shapiro and Milner.

21

"You think you'll find that son of a bitch?" Diane asked Steinberg as they sat in the lounge of the El Capitan.

"I don't know. I'm sure going to try."

"Did you check his room?"

"I just went up there about ten minutes ago and knocked. No answer. I think he must have taken off."

"And left all his things?"

"I don't know. I just can't figure it out."

"Maybe he's still in town; maybe you'll find him."

"Maybe." Steinberg called the waitress over and ordered two drinks. He looked around the casino. It was filled to capacity—the dinner show had broken just a few minutes before. All the tables were open and in full swing, and the crowds streamed around the casino. The place glittered.

"You think I ought to get out of Vegas?" Diane asked.

"Where would you go?"

"I don't know. Anywhere. Maybe go to LA."

"What would you do there?"

"That's the trouble, Don. I don't know how to make a living. Here in Vegas, I can make good bread. I made $600 last night with this guy from Norfolk; he's a friend of a guy who once bought me a car. We played here and at the Sands. And I was really nervous, because you have to be super careful at the Sands. It's almost as bad as the Hilton. I could tell you some horror stories about the Hilton."

"I got barred at the Hilton last night; did I tell you?"

"No shit? Barred?"

"Yes, on top of everything, after not getting any money from Thornton, they barred me. I guess we were too conspicuous, and the fucker kept asking me about the card count. 'What's the goddamn count?' he kept asking in a loud fucking voice. He was shouting those words around the room."

"He must be a real asshole. I'm sorry."

"What are you sorry about?"

"For giving him your number."

"Jesus, you meant well. And it could have worked out into something good. I was going to give you a piece of the action."

"You don't have to."

"Well, I was." Steinberg stood up and looked towards the craps pit. "I thought I saw the bastard. I hate this constant looking for him."

Their drinks came.

"I figured with that money, Diane, with that five or six thousand, I'd hit the $100 tables, go after that big money myself. That was my plan. Now, I'm in the same goddamn boat I was in before."

"What are you going to do?"

"I don't know. I'm getting sick and tired of playing twenty-one. Sick and tired of the tables and of Vegas. I feel like moving on."

"You think you really want to leave Vegas?"

He shrugged. "Yes . . . Paula and I used to go up to New England . . . up to the Cape . . . I've been thinking of that place again, and of upstate New York."

"Oh . . ."

"I don't know . . . I need a change of scenery. Somewhere near the sea, or in the country, that would be nice."

Diane grew quiet. She stirred her Dewar's, and fooled

around with the stirrer. "Suppose I decided to leave Vegas, Don? Could you see me going with you?"

"What?"

"You heard me. Would you go with me?"

"The two of us. As a team?"

"Yes. You think it'd work out?"

"I don't know. I never thought of us that way. You're my friend and all . . ."

"Well, it's good to have a friend. To be with a friend."

"Sure it is." He drank some of the Wild Turkey, trying to clear his head of the residue of fatigue that hung there like a wet rag.

"Anyway, just a passing thought," said Diane. "I'll probably never leave Vegas. I keep thinking about bringing my kid to live with me. I may do it, Don. I may do it. I nearly called my mother yesterday. Nearly did."

"It would be a good move."

"Yes," she said, "it would be a good move."

They watched the crowds in the casino jamming the aisles, crowding the tables.

"You know," said Steinberg, "I was thinking. Thornton mentioned to me that he had a deal . . . some arrangement with a dealer here, in the El Capitan."

"What kind of deal?"

"He worked out something . . . something about a dealer signaling his hole card to him."

"No shit. Which dealer?"

"I forgot. Can you believe it? The bastard even mentioned his name, something like Ed, I just can't remember. So much was going on at the Hilton . . . I should have burned that name into my brain."

"What are you going to do tonight? Stay here and look for Thornton?"

"I don't know. I hate to hang around, waiting for him to show. He might be home by now for all I know."

"Don, I'm going to take off soon. I'm supposed to meet Cindy tonight at the Frontier."

"She really hangs around there, doesn't she?"

"Yeah, she screws one of the pitbosses to stay there. Otherwise, no way. I'll be taking off soon. Give me a kiss, Don."

He bent over and kissed her, then leaned back and touched her face gently. "I'm going to look around this place one more time," he said.

He got up and pushed his way through the mob of people surrounding the tables. He checked out the craps pit, baccarat, the keno lounge, and the slots area. No sign of Thornton. Steinberg strolled slowly past the blackjack pit, looking over the games, hoping to find him but knowing in his heart that Thornton wasn't going to be playing twenty-one here—not with his money.

He paused and watched the $100 table. Four players were at the table, but the third baseman's seat was empty. One of the players, sitting in the second seat, was playing two hands at a time and really raking in the checks. He not only had black $100 checks but whole piles of pink $500 ones.

Steinberg tried to see what was going on, but the crowds were too dense. A security guard was keeping order. When there was a break in the game he looked at the dealer, who was reshuffling the four decks. Steinberg narrowed his eyes, trying to make out the name on the dealer's tag. The name he saw was Teddy.

Teddy. Teddy. It rang a bell. That was the bastard Thornton had mentioned. Was Thornton at the table? No . . . but that big winner, maybe he was the one now getting the signals . . . maybe.

Steinberg took out his cash and counted it. He had only $600, hardly enough for a $100 game. Scared money. Still, that third baseman's seat was open. He took a deep breath and made his way through the crowd. The security guard let him pass when he saw that Steinberg was a player.

Don pushed his way into the seat and readjusted it, trying to get comfortable. The cards were being put into the shoe. Steinberg took out his money. He got six black checks for the cash, and put one out into his betting box.

Teddy slid out the first card and burned it, putting it out of play, into a plastic case. The game was on.

All the cards were dealt open. Steinberg's first card was a 4, the second a 5 for a 9. The dealer showed a 6. He had to double down. Another black check went out. His card was dealt open. It was a 4. He was in deep trouble unless the dealer busted. The man who was the big winner had stood with 17 and 20 totals, without drawing a card.

The dealer had an ace in the hole for a 17 and Steinberg was left with four black checks. He could feel his heart pumping. This was the first time he had bet black checks with his own money, and maybe he was crazy, he told himself, maybe Thornton had bullshitted him, maybe this was the wrong dealer. It was absolutely crazy, but he had to go on and see what happened.

On the next hand, he got a 10, 5 for 15. The dealer showed an 8. There'd be no signal now, because to give a signal, the dealer had to peek, and he couldn't peek at the hole card with an 8 showing. Steinberg watched the big winner bust on a 10, 3 that he hit, and stand on a 19. Now it was his turn. He had no choice but to hit the hard 15. He pointed at his cards for a hit and got a king. Busted that hand. Now he had three checks left. He put one out again. Each was a hundred dollars, and a hundred dollars was a lot of money. He could do better things with a hundred dollars than piss it away on this insane hunch.

The cards were dealt again. His first card was an ace. Come on, he prayed silently, give me a 10 for blackjack.

But he was dealt a 3 for soft 14. The dealer showed a 6. Another double-down situation.

Should he or shouldn't he? The dealer waited patiently for Steinberg to make a decision on the cards. Steinberg put down another black check and doubled down. He got a 10 for 14. A dead hand.

The dealer turned over a 2 and hit a 9 for 17. Steinberg was now down to one black check. In three deals he had lost $500. In three deals and five minutes.

He put out his last check. Now or never. His first card was an 8. The second card was an 8. The dealer showed a 9 as his upcard.

Shit, this was it. He was supposed to split the 8s, but he was out of money, and he had no credit at the El Capitan. And he didn't even have a check with him, nothing.

A sure loser, this 16. The dealer waited for him to make a move, and Steinberg, against his better judgment, decided to stand on the lousy 16. He waved his right hand over the cards, and got ready to leave the table.

The dealer turned over a 4 in the hole for 13, hit an ace for 14, and a deuce for 16. Instead of dealing another card, he rearranged them, and recounted the total. Steinberg could feel his heart pounding through his mouth. *Keep cool, keep cool,* he told himself, but he felt like shouting for joy when the dealer busted with a king.

Steinberg had been pulled out of the grave at the very last minute. He could feel the sweat on his back, in his crotch, sliding down the sides of his body. He was being wrung out by this stupid game, and he still didn't know if there was a signal being passed.

The cocktail waitress came by, and the men at the table ordered drinks, causing a slight break in the action. Steinberg ordered a Kahlúa-and-cream and a glass of water on the side. He needed something soothing.

The game went on. On the next hand, Steinberg put one check out, all he dared bet. His first card was an ace. He prayed hard for the 10, but got a 9 for 20. Good enough. The dealer showed a king. He peeked. The big winner didn't look anywhere but at the dealer's face. The dealer didn't look at the big winner.

The player Steinberg had been watching wore a black shirt stitched with silver flowers, open almost to the navel. A gold razor blade hung from a chain around his neck. He was in his late twenties or thereabouts, thought Steinberg, and he slightly resembled Mick Jagger, with the same loose kind of face.

The winner held two bust hands, 13 and 14. He hit the first and got an 8 for 21, and hit the second and got a 3 for 17.

Steinberg was holding his 20 and had to stand. The dealer had a 9 in the hole for 19, and paid off Steinberg.

On the next hand, the winner was dealt a 15 and a 20. Teddy peeked under his 10. The winner stood on both hands. Steinberg held a 10, 2, a sure hit against the dealer's 10. He took a deep breath and stood.

Teddy had a 6 underneath and busted. So there it was, thought Steinberg, there it was. This was the dude getting the signal. He'd just follow him. There was no reason why this guy would hit bust cards on one play and stand on them on the second play unless he was playing hunches, or unless he got a signal about that hole card. And the dude was winning too much to be a hunch player. Still, Steinberg told himself, that idiot Thornton had won on hunches.

A new player shoved his way in, sitting in the vacant seat to the big winner's left. He was a silver-haired man, looking sleek as a greyhound in a blue sharkskin suit. He asked for a marker for $10,000.

The floorman, who had been watching the game, asked his name.

"Jessup. I'm with the Brass junket."

"Give him the ten," the floorman instructed the dealer. There was a slight delay while the marker was signed and the checks were handed over. The new player started out with a $1,000 bet, the same betting range as the big winner, who piled on 10 black checks on each of his betting boxes.

After a few more deals, Steinberg knew that the big winner wasn't playing hunches at all. He never made a wrong play when Teddy peeked at the hole card. What the signal was, Steinberg couldn't figure out, but it was there. And he took advantage of it, mimicking the play of the big winner.

The cards were so-so. Steinberg clawed his way back to his original $600, but Jessup had to get another marker for $10,000 within ten minutes. The game was heating up. And then Teddy went on his break.

Steinberg was tempted to leave the table, but he didn't want to give up the third baseman's seat. The big winner, however, took a walk, telling the floorman to watch his checks. He came back fifteen minutes later, and Teddy returned five minutes after that. During that time, Steinberg held his own. He still had his $600. Meanwhile he had gone through four glasses of water and the same number of King Alfonsos and Kahlúa-and-creams.

With Teddy back, the big winner began betting a thousand a hand again. The game was back in full blast.

Steinberg continued to mimic the player getting the signal but couldn't figure it out. The dealer never looked at the big winner except to deal to him. Something was happening, but what? And what difference did the actual signal matter, as long as he could use it?

He moved ahead, up to $400 in winnings. Then he doubled his money. Soon he was at $1,500 in checks. Then, protected by the big winner's play, Steinberg increased his bets to $200. Then $300. Jessup had disappeared from the table, having lost all of his original $20,000. His place was taken by another member of Brass's junket, who took a marker for $5,000 and whose hands shook every time he made a bet.

At two in the morning, when the swing shift ended, Steinberg was ahead over $5,000. It was the biggest win of his life. He stayed for a couple of more hands after Teddy was relieved, then got up and cashed in.

He was dead tired, and not even the elation accompanying the win could hold off the fatigue. He called Thornton's room one more time and hung up bitterly when there was no response. He'd get him, but right now, first things first.

Steinberg picked up his car at valet service and drove home, barely able to keep his eyes open.

22

"Hello, there. Remember me?"

Diane looked up at the middle-aged man who was standing by the table, smiling. She narrowed her eyes, trying to place him.

"My name's Harry. Does that ring a bell?"

"Harry . . ."

"Last night. You got stuck with your car, ran out of gas. You have a big Lincoln, don't you?"

"Oh, yes. Jesus, I forgot all about it."

"Mind if I sit down?"

"No, go ahead."

"What are you drinking?"

"A Dewar's."

"You want another?"

"OK."

Milner called the waitress over and ordered two Scotches.

"I owe you something," he said. He took out a fifty-dollar bill from his pocket.

"What's this for?"

"You left two El Capitan quarter checks in my car that night. This is yours."

"Hey, watch the way you give it to me; some security guard will think I'm a hooker."

"Don't worry about it. I work here, remember?"

"Oh, yes."

The drinks came. Milner signed the tab and gave the girl a dollar.

"That's right," said Diane. "I remember you saying something about working here."

"Yes, in the back office. It's just a job. Let me ask you a question, OK?"

"Sure."

"Your name is Diane, right? Is that right?"

"That's my name."

"You hang around a lot in here, don't you?"

"Well, I live in town. I hang around a lot of places, you know. This is a small town."

"That's right. What do you do for a living, Diane?"

"Why do you ask?"

"Just curious."

She drank a little of the Scotch and looked at Milner over the rim of the glass, but didn't answer. Finally she asked, "You think I'm a hooker?"

"No."

"Then why did you ask?"

"You asked me what I did."

"I didn't ask you. You told me."

He drank some of his own drink, and jiggled an ice cube in his mouth. "That's right. You're right. You didn't ask."

"Are you annoyed that I'm here, is that it?" Diane asked.

"No, why should I be?"

"Well, you're looking at me in this strange way. And asking me all these questions."

"You're really touchy tonight, aren't you?"

"Maybe. I've got a right to be."

"Is it about your boyfriend?"

"What boyfriend?"

"You were telling me about him when we first met."

"What boyfriend? I don't have a boyfriend."

Milner shrugged. He could see how hostile she was, and he stood up. "Well, anyway, I wanted to give you back the money."

"Thanks. I appreciate it."

"I guess I'll be taking off."

She didn't say anything.

Milner got up and walked slowly through the casino. It was packed now, so different from the beginning of the week when it resembled a morgue. There was plenty of action; the tables were all open and the crowds were busting the place at its seams.

He went to the front door and the valet ran for his car. Milner lit a cigarette, realizing how bad a mood he was in. Diane had really sensed it. Boy, he had really jumped on her. He had lost his cool with her. Milner shook his head.

He thought back over the day. The meeting with English. Enough to drive anyone through the roof. And calling Mary till almost midnight, and still no answer in Denver. Well, the marriage was breaking up and had been breaking up for a long time. Let it go.

His car came around. He got in and drove off, still thinking about Diane. There was something she said that disturbed him, but he didn't know what, or where it was coming from in himself. He blotted her out of his mind, thinking that he had to go somewhere, be with some people.

Milner remembered Chet's invitation and headed east, toward Barcelona, where Chet lived. Fifteen minutes later, he was at the house and parking in front. He walked around the side toward the pool, but no one was there, and although lights were on in the house, he didn't want to disturb the Gardners. Maybe it was a mistake showing up without calling first.

Milner was about to get back into the car when he heard his name called. Chet was standing by the front door, holding a drink.

"Harry, is that you? Wait a minute." Chet trotted down the path to the car. "Harry, why don't you come in for a drink?"

"No thanks."

"Come on. We can sit in the back by the pool."

Harry followed Gardner into the house. Gardner's kids were watching TV and didn't even look up at him. Grace was in the kitchen, making some sandwiches.

"Like a sandwich?" she asked.

"No thanks. How are things, Grace?"

"Oh, very well. The kids are going fishing tomorrow at Lake Mead, so I'm making them some sandwiches. I have plenty, though. Care for peanut butter and jelly, or ham and cheese?"

"No thanks."

"What do you want to drink?" Chet asked.

"Oh . . . do you have any brandy?"

"Sure thing. How about some cognac? Got some good Three-Star Hennessy."

"That sounds good."

"On the rocks?"

"Fine."

Milner sat on a plastic chair on the patio, near the pool. He yawned, then lit a cigarette. Around him the night was dark and silent, except for the strains of some music from a nearby house. He looked up at the sky and the stars. So mysterious, that dark sky.

That sky. This night. That was what he loved about the West, the big sky, the blackness of it at night. He couldn't bear to live in the crowded East anymore; he couldn't be hemmed in. He needed this kind of space.

Chet came out with the glasses and the brandy.

Milner drank some. "It's real good stuff," he told Chet.

"Yes, picked it up at Wonderworld. They have a great discount liquor store there."

"I know. I used to live around there, near Twain. I used to stop off and get that Baskin-Robbins ice cream at the store there."

"It's still there."

"Some things never change," he said, "and some things change." He didn't know why he was saying this, or what significance it had. Just something welling up inside him. Maybe it was thinking of Mary in Denver, or Grace making those sandwiches. "Watching Grace in there, you know, Chet, it reminded me of when I was a kid. My father would take me and my younger brother crabbing in Chesapeake Bay, and my mother would do what Grace was doing, fix sandwiches, usually the night before. She had this specialty, ham salad with sliced onions. Don't ask me why that combination, but that's what she made, God bless her. I guess my father loved onions. He'd have onions with everything, even plain onion sandwiches."

"My father was the same way about cucumbers," Chet said. "We had a plot of land near Omaha, and he'd plant his hills of cucumbers. I got sick of cucumbers and tomatoes. Those were the things he planted year after year. I had a little patch of my own, so I grew something different. Kentucky Wonder green beans, and swiss chard and spinach. I liked chard and spinach in salads. I guess when I was a kid, I ate pretty healthy foods, all those vegetables. And we raised chickens. I was at the doctor's the other day and he told me my cholesterol was a little too high. Also the blood pressure. But if I was back at the farm, Harry, I'd be a healthy man today."

"Your parents still live there?"

"No, my father died some years back and my mother is living with one of my sisters in Kansas City."

"My father's dead too. Jesus, the men don't last too long, do they? My mother is still in Baltimore, still in the same old house. She has some women cousins living with her, so it isn't too lonely for her. I always ask her if she wants to come out here. The weather might be better for her, but she doesn't want to leave that house."

"I've never been to Baltimore. What's it like?"

"It's different now, from when I was a kid. Much different. But it was a great place to grow up. We lived in the Dundalk section, and that was a little world of its own. And Baltimore had some good things going for it. The restaurants . . . they had some of the best restaurants there . . . Hausner's and Chesapeake House and Miller Brothers. That was my favorite, Miller Brothers. Good seafood, good American food. You know what I miss most about the east? The seafood."

One of the kids called Chet, and he excused himself and went into the house.

Milner helped himself to more cognac. It was good stuff, all right. He put down the glass and lit another cigarette, coughing violently. Goddamn cigarettes. It was too dark to see his fingers, but he knew they were tobacco-stained. He'd have to cut down.

The casino was still in his thoughts, even out here. No way to stop those thoughts, any more than he could stop smoking cigarettes. Images flooded through his mind; Moe Lewis and Tiny Shapiro and Leon Balofsky, the room where the meeting was held. No, he didn't want to think about it anymore.

He got up and walked to the edge of the patio, standing by the redwood fence. The lights in the next house were out, but the distant music was still playing. He tried to catch the sounds in order, to pick out the melody, but they were too remote, too disconnected.

He looked up at the sky again. Dark black, the sky over Vegas was so black. So distant . . . He wondered what Vegas looked like from a star. It would look like nothing at all, just be nothing to look at. *Hell, what am I thinking,* Milner thought, *the whole goddamn Earth would look like nothing from a star.*

Milner closed his eyes and pictured the casino. Couldn't get away from it. Just couldn't. Opening them again, he turned away from the fence, and could see Chet in the kitchen, with one of his boys. He thought of Chet in the office, telling him that it was their job to destroy people. Chet suffered in the job. He had nearly quit a few times and now he had high blood pressure. He let the job affect him too much. Maybe Chet was too decent a guy for the job. In the casinos, you needed ice water in your veins; you had to be cold as ice.

Destroy people. The name George Farkas flashed through Milner's brain. George Farkas. That was the name he had tried to obliterate from his memory, but it flashed in his mind time and again, a neon sign in the hell of his unconscious. George Farkas.

He had first met Farkas in the Tropicana, and they became friends quickly. He met Farkas's family, the wife, the two boys, the daughter—they'd always stay at the Trop. Farkas followed Milner to his new hotel, and then, when

Milner took over the El Capitan, he followed him there too.

Farkas had been an A player for many years, a premium player no matter how you looked at him. He was sought after by all the hotels, but he stayed loyal to Milner. And Milner always made sure that he and his family had special treatment. Always the best rooms, the best service, special gifts for his kids.

Slowly but surely the losses took their toll, and when Farkas's business ran into a recession and hit the skids, Farkas found himself in deep financial trouble. It didn't stop his playing, but he couldn't afford to take the beatings at the table anymore. Farkas went into debt, first borrowing from banks, and when that source dried up, from the loan sharks. He was sliding toward disaster.

Milner tried to reason with him, but it was no use. If he tried to cut Farkas's credit off, there were a dozen hotels willing to take him on. So, Milner tempered his friendship with his business sense, and let Farkas play at the tables, on credit. The inevitable happened. The loan sharks started to move into his business, and, as a last desperate measure, the Greek took out a large mortgage on his home and with the money hit the El Capitan and its craps tables.

He hit them, all right. As Milner watched in his office on the closed-circuit TV set, Farkas beat the tables for close to fifty big ones. He wanted the limit raised. Milner knew that if he did this Farkas would eventually lose it all again, because no table stayed hot all the time. The law of large numbers, which Milner was very familiar with, would prevail. But Milner also knew that the win was affecting the drop and p.c. at the tables, was hurting his business. So his decision was strictly a business one. He raised the limits. He could have reasoned with Farkas then, told him to stop playing, but instead, he raised the limits.

What if he had spoken to the Greek? What difference would it have made at that time? None, but the point was he didn't speak to him, nor did he speak to him when Farkas had $150,000 of their money. He sent Chet to speak to him. The Greek told the credit manager that he was going after a half million, that it was sure as shooting that he'd have it in another few hours at the table. He wanted the limits raised again. This time, Milner called Balofsky and explained the situation. Mr. B told him to raise the limits one more time. Mr. B's theory was similar to Milner's; the Greek would burn himself out, and tired, would play recklessly and lose it all back. He had already spent twenty-four hours at the table.

It would have been so easy for Milner to go to the table, to put his arm around Farkas and tell him, "Friend, call it quits, take the money and leave Vegas for good. Think of your family. Don't lose the house, the business. Take the money and God bless you."

But Milner stayed glued to the TV set, watching the action. He decided that he'd go to Farkas when Farkas was down to the original $50,000 in winnings. But who could tell at what point that occurred?

He knew in his heart that he wasn't looking at Farkas as a friend, but as a customer, just another player. For a while, during the next day, Farkas increased his win, but the tide turned, as it always did. Farkas bet more heavily as the dice turned on him, and Milner finally shut off the TV set when Farkas changed color with his last black check and covered all the hardways, then rolled a 7. It was all over.

Farkas came into the office and asked for more credit. One last chance to get even. Milner shook his head. Farkas sat in front of him, gray, broke, his face ravaged by the two days of continuous play.

"I'll give you twenty-five grand credit," he told the Greek, "on one condition. You take it and pay off the mortgage, and fly out of town."

"Twenty-five big ones won't cover it," said Farkas. "Harry, give me one more chance at the tables. I need big money."

"I can't, George. Your credit here is used up."

Milner was on solid ground. He knew the Greek couldn't get a penny anywhere else in Vegas. He was washed up in the town. He wasn't an A player anymore; he was merely another loser in the land of losers.

Farkas left the office. Milner told himself that he'd done all he could. He'd offered him the twenty-five big ones. How could he run a casino and be friends with the players at the same time? He just couldn't do both; he knew he needed that ice in his veins to do his job right.

Farkas cut his throat the next day. When the two Farkas boys arrived for the body, they came to Milner's office and stared at the president of the hotel. They said nothing, just stared. Milner couldn't look them in the eyes. For the first time in his life, he couldn't look someone in the eyes.

Milner held the empty glass and stared into space, into the darkness of the desert night. *What could you do with these compulsive players?,* he asked himself. He had done all that anyone else would have done.

But he wasn't anyone else. He was Farkas's friend. And he'd thought of other things before he thought of friendship. Milner could rationalize all he wanted to, but in his heart he knew he hadn't really tried to do the right thing.

No wonder Chet has high blood pressure. One of these days, something will hit me, too. It was as sure as the dice turning, as the house percentages. Milner went back to his chair and sat down again, closing his eyes, trying to ease his mind.

Saturday

23

"Yes, but you don't understand," Thornton said, speaking to his wife on the phone. "Yes, I'm in Los Angeles, but there was some mixup at the hotel and I moved into a Motel 6. It's cheaper anyway . . . No, it doesn't really matter, because I'll be leaving Sunday. Only one more day . . . No, I haven't made a reservation on the flight; I'll call you as soon as I get one . . . Yes, definitely." He held the phone a few inches from his left ear, hearing his wife go on about problems. Then he spoke again. "Give Wendy my love. Tell her I miss her . . . Yes, I'll bring her back something."

But the conversation wasn't over yet. His wife had several messages from her father about affairs at the office. Thornton listened to them, feeling his whole body shudder. Finally, the conversation came to an end, and he hung up the phone. The call to his wife, the messages from his father-in-law, the whole thought of his home life in Chicago lay heavy upon his soul. The very mention of the flight back depressed him. What was the point of returning to Chicago? What awaited him there but misery? If he had any guts, he wouldn't go back. He'd go to California or someplace else, and end the charade that was his present existence. It would be difficult only because of Wendy, who was now seven, but other men had left their children; it was possible to do this and lead a normal life.

It was almost eight in the morning, and he was downtown, standing in the outer lobby of the Golden Nugget, near the rear parking lot. The call had upset his stomach, and he told himself that he shouldn't have called right after breakfast. But he had put off the call for a couple of days, and knew he had to make it. Luckily the men's room was nearby, and after a bad case of runs, Thornton washed his hands and face and went in search of the gift shop, where he could get some mints or gum.

He hadn't returned to the El Capitan since the night he left Steinberg at the Hilton, and he saw no reason to go back, except for one thing. His money was still in the safe-deposit box in the El Capitan's cashier's cage, and sooner or later he'd have to figure a way to get in and get that money without Steinberg finding him.

That night, that crazy night at the Hilton, Thornton had won close to $25,000. The thought of giving away more than $8,000 of it was depressing. He had better use for the money than Steinberg; with a run of good luck he could turn it into $100,000. Even if he lost $8,000, that would make him even, if he imagined that Steinberg had been given his share.

Right now he was staying in a motel in the downtown section, off Fremont. It was a dump, but what did that matter? The important thing was that it was hidden away in a section where Steinberg would never look for him.

Thornton had rented a blue Chevy Nova, which gave him mobility. And he had given the rental people a deposit and told them he would deliver the car to the airport at LA. He'd worked out everything.

The only obstacle was getting his money out of the El Capitan. But he'd do it. Screw Steinberg. He didn't deserve his share, if the truth were told. It wasn't Steinberg who had made the big money; he was too conservative with his stupid counts. If Steinberg had controlled the betting, at best they would have won a couple of thousand dollars. And he didn't need Steinberg in the first place. The game was a matter of luck, and the cards had fallen right for him that night. He had held a hot hand.

Getting the money from the Hilton had been simple. Later that morning Thornton had returned to the Hilton and cashed in about three thousand in the black checks that he had carried out of the casino. He'd taken a chance, but he figured that Steinberg would be waiting for him back at the El Capitan.

Thornton was still registered there, but they could keep the lousy suitcase and the clothing and shaving cream for all he cared. Maybe, before he left Vegas, he'd call and ask them to mail the whole bundle to Chicago. No, that would be too risky. If Betty ever saw a package arrive from Vegas, the game would be up. He'd forget about the junk he left there. All that remained now was to make good use of the money he had won, to run it into a fortune. That would not only wipe out his debts, but leave him with plenty besides. Already, in Thornton's mind, the idea of taking off and starting a new life was ripening. This would be his ultimate fantasy. A new identity, with about sixty or seventy thousand in cash to tide him over. He'd just vanish from Chicago. The thought now overwhelmed him; he was excited the way he had never been excited before.

He bought some Life Savers at the gift shop and walked to the keno lounge and sat down. He chewed on a Life Saver, thinking. What could be more thrilling than disappearing and starting a new life? First, he'd return to Chicago. He had some debts that had to be paid; about $20,000 worth. Then, with the rest of the cash—cash nobody knew about—he would disappear one bright morning. On the way to work. Even if news of his gambling came out, all they'd figure was that the underworld had disposed of him. It was perfect.

A new identity. He could assume a new image, a completely new lifestyle. He could let his hair grow long, grow a mustache, maybe even a beard, wear tinted glasses, put on jeans and boots. Who would know him or recognize him? Maybe he could take up with some young chick. He was still young enough for that; he had a full year to go before his fortieth birthday. It all could be done, and California, which seemed the best place for his new life, was near Vegas. He could come here any day of the week he wanted action.

The thought of a young woman to share this future life caused him to look over a pretty young blond who sat two seats over. She caught his gaze and smiled at him. *Jesus,* he thought, *she's no older than nineteen, if that old. What the hell.* Thornton moved over and sat next to her, expecting her to become annoyed. But she smiled at him again.

"Hi," he said.

"Hi."

"Playing keno?" he asked. She had a couple of tickets in her hand and was scanning the keno board.

"Yeah, but I didn't catch anything. Just two numbers. This is a hard game to win anything at."

"They're all hard."

"You visiting?" she asked.

"Yes. I'm from Chicago. How about yourself?"

"I live here."

"Really?"

"Yeah, for six months now. I rent a trailer. They're pretty cheap."

"A trailer?"

"In a trailer park."

"Oh, yes."

A new keno game was going on. She marked her ticket and went to the keno writer, then returned to her former seat.

"How long you visiting?" she asked.

"Oh, for a few more days. My name's Lee, by the way."

"I'm Patti."

"What do you do in Vegas?" he asked.

"Me? I'm a working girl."

"Oh." He didn't quite know what she meant. The new numbers were flashing on the board and she concentrated on them. Thornton looked her over from close range. She had blue eyes and short blond hair and a really pretty face, the face of an Iowa farmer's daughter.

"Where you from originally?" he asked.

"Wisconsin. Madison."

Thornton nodded.

"Geez, none of the numbers caught. Can you believe that?" Patti asked. "I got no luck at all."

"Well, it's a rough game, as you said. Why don't we get out of here?"

"You want to party?"

"Huh?" He hadn't expected such a flagrant invitation.

"Party. You know . . ."

"All right . . . uh, do you . . . charge?"

He felt embarrassed asking this, but how could he figure her out so soon?

"Sure. I told you, I'm a working girl."

"What do you charge?"

"Thirty-five."

"Thirty-five?"

"Look," Patti said, "I'll tell you what. It's morning, and I usually don't work this early. Tell you what. Twenty-five. But that's it."

"Where do you live?"

"Over by Boulder. You want to go to your place?"

"Uh . . . no."

"You got your wife with you?"

"No." He had the money stashed in the room, carefully taped behind the dresser.

"Why don't you want to go to your room, then?"

"Uh . . . you know. I have some people who know me there."

"Where you staying?"

"Uh . . . nearby. Why can't we go to your place?"

"We can, but it's a long ride."

"So what? How long can it be? I have a car."

"You can follow me then. I got one also. It's parked in back, in the lot."

He drove slowly down Fremont, following the black '62 Ford. At Boulder, she made a right turn and they went past the Showboat Hotel, which he had never seen before. It looked like an apparition out here, so far from any of the other casinos.

They drove for a couple of miles up Boulder, and then she turned into a trailer park and he followed the car through winding turns, past kids playing in the dirt. He had never been inside a trailer park before, and it looked like a scene from a grade-B movie, with old people sitting outside, kids in the dust, an air of calm defeat.

She parked in front of a green and white trailer, and showed him where he could park the Nova. He kicked up dust as he walked, and went up the steps to her trailer, ducking under a low-slung plastic canopy.

"It's nothing fancy," she said, "but it's OK."

The rooms were small and narrow, and he felt hemmed in by the place.

"Make yourself at home. Want a cold drink?"

"OK."

She served him a root beer, and he drank from the bottle, nearly gagging at the taste. He put down the bottle as she passed by, and put his arms around her waist.

"Wait a minute, OK? About the $25."

"Oh, sure."

He got out his wallet and gave her a twenty and a five. She excused herself and went into the bedroom, then came out again, in her panties and bra. She had a nice figure, a young girl's figure. He was tempted to ask her how old she was. Her legs were thin and milky white, and her breasts were firm and round.

"Come on inside. We can do it on the bed."

He took off his clothes, and she got off her bra and panties. The sight of that young body was too much for Thornton. He fell upon her, kissing her neck, her shoulders, her breasts, her stomach. He could taste the salty flesh, and it drove him wild.

His lips moved down her stomach, to the edge of her pubic hair, but she pushed his head away with her hand.

"I don't like my cunt eaten," Patti said.

The word "cunt" made him shake. He couldn't stop shaking. God, he needed this. He went inside her and started pumping, and within a minute he had come. He lay upon her, exhausted, but she told him he was too heavy, so he turned over on his side.

"Look, I don't want to rush you or anything," Patti said, "but I got another appointment soon."

Thornton slowly got up.

"Listen, what's your name again?"

"Lee."

"Lee, you interested in buying something?"

"What?"

"Wait a minute." She returned with a revolver.

"It's a Smith and Wesson .38. It's a good gun."

He looked it over and opened it up. The chambers were empty.

"It comes with a box of shells."

"Whose is this?"

"It's my boyfriend's. He needs money. He's in the county jail right now."

"Why?"

"He got caught at the El Capitan, fooling around with the slots. He needs bail money."

"You should be making enough."

"Yeah . . . but you know, I got busted myself last week, and it costs a $150 to get out; that's what it costs for the bondsman and the lawyer. It's a nice gun, isn't it?"

"Yes, good clean gun."

"You can have it for $75."

"I don't know."

"Sixty. But that's it. You go into a gun store and it costs $150."

"I'll think about it."

"Well, I got no phone. But you can come here. Just knock three times. Then I'll open up."

Thornton left a few minutes later. His legs felt weak, but it wasn't a bad feeling. He wished he hadn't come so fast. She was really a delicious bitch. It was worth it. He could feel himself getting an erection as he drove back downtown.

24

John Holland lit a cigarette with shaking fingers, then carefully closed the cover of the lighter and put it into his pocket. He blew out some smoke, and leaned against the railing in his private domain, the mezzanine level whose floor contained the one-way mirrors that overlooked the entire El Capitan casino, the "eye in the sky."

Holland took a break. He had been at the post for about an hour, moving slowly along the walkways, looking down through the mirrors and watching the various tables. He had concentrated on craps 3, which he had been told was having poor drops and p.c.s throughout this swing shift.

He closed his eyes, still seeing the bright colors of the casino below him, the figures blurred into sliding patterns, the men and women playing, the dealers, the floormen, the pitbosses, the strays walking through the casino. He had been seeing all this from his unique perch for the last five years, and sometimes his eyes would ache for hours. It wasn't a normal perspective, looking down the way he did. Half the time he was on his knees to get a better look at what was going on. And in all the time he had been up here, all these years, he'd seen only a few examples of cheating, mostly in the slots area, where amateurs tried to jolt some coins out of disobedient machines. When this happened, he would get right in touch with security and Derringer, then he would watch the action on the floor, as the cheats were grabbed. It was usually done fast and without anyone being aware of what was going on, because Derringer's office was nearby, and the people were simply hustled there.

With the table games he was extra careful, because cheating wasn't that flagrant, and he had to watch closely to spot something wrong. At the slots, he could see a cheat shoving some kind of objects into a machine, but the table games involved hands and arms and mostly rhythm. That's what he looked for—a break in the rhythm, something out of the ordinary.

He had found this several times over the years. Once, a group made a concerted effort to steal casino checks from the craps tables, especially the very crowded ones. One agent would push into a player while the other would grab checks off his rail, while yet a third would create a disturbance at another part of the table. The three were quickly caught. They hadn't realized they could be so easily observed from the one-way mirrors above the table. But from where Holland was perched, it was such a flagrant situation—the rhythm of the table having changed so abruptly—that they might as well have been shooting off rockets.

Whenever Holland saw any kind of upsetting motion, he immediately looked to the other side of the table, to where all was calm and placid. A few years back there was a craps dealer passing off checks. While a commotion was stirred up at the other end of the table, the dealer quickly handed off quarter and $100 checks to a confederate posing as a legitimate player. In this case Holland easily spotted the passing off. He called down to the floor, got hold of both the pitboss and Moe Lewis, and in a few minutes five men were watching the dealer.

They nailed both of them, and what happened afterwards, Holland could only guess at. He never heard of any prosecutions, so the bosses must have taken care of it in their own way.

But these were isolated cases in a long career of looking and watching. The casino bosses had many internal methods of protecting their bankroll, and perhaps, where real thievery could go on—in the cage and the counting room—the TV cameras were doing just as good a job of watching as Holland. At least, he figured, those cameras never blinked, never took breaks and had no loyalties that could be compromised.

Because of his job, Holland stayed aloof from the dealers and the floormen, men he had worked with before. He couldn't get close to any of them and still do his work efficiently. He didn't want the day to come where he saw a friend cheat the house and would have to turn him in. So he had a whole circle of friends who had nothing to do with the El Capitan casino.

The El Capitan made good use of the eye in the sky, by constantly having someone up there. Just out of curiosity, Holland had visited a couple of other eyes in other casinos, and some of them were covered with dust and cobwebs. It was up to the men on the floor in those places to watch the bankroll, since the eye in the sky was kept simply as a deterrent. Some casinos relied only on the TV cameras. Here, at the El Capitan, security had always been of the utmost importance. Not only did they have the eye in the sky, but cameras were on all the time, tuned to every table, to every part of the casino.

Most of the time, Holland's assignment was to look for other things besides cheating. He watched for dealers hustling for tokes, intimidating players into betting for them, or being hostile when tokes weren't forthcoming. Since Milner had taken over, this was particularly frowned upon. Holland had been in other casinos where craps players were always being hustled to make bets for the dealers. He had had that experience a couple of times and stayed away from the craps pits in those places.

When he first came to Vegas, he did more playing than he did now, and he remembered avoiding one downtown casino for a number of years because of one dealer who continually pushed him for tokes. He could understand why Milner was so strict about this. It hurt business; it hurt everyone involved in the casino.

When Holland caught this kind of hustling, he reported it immediately to Moe Lewis, who consulted with the shift boss and the pitboss. Usually, they spoke to the dealer and warned him, but after a couple of warnings, the dealer was out on his ass. And these dealers never knew how they were found out. They thought the customers complained (which they rarely did), or the boxman had picked it up, or a floorman had overheard them. They never realized that John Holland, in the eye in the sky, was always alert, always listening, always watching.

He ground out the cigarette and walked back to the craps area, standing over craps 3. The table was packed tonight, as was the casino, despite the fact that the show had already begun and had absorbed the huge line of people waiting to see it.

There were footsteps coming up the stairs. Holland looked to the door, and Moe Lewis and Harry Milner entered.

"How's it going, John?" Milner asked.

"All right, Mr. Milner. Nothing much happening, but you've got one busy casino down there."

"Yes, sweet to see all those warm bodies. What were you just watching?"

"Craps 3."

"Good. Keep an eye on that goddamn table." Milner looked around. Moe Lewis had drifted off to the blackjack section and was standing at a railing, smoking his cigar, watching the pit below.

Milner watched the action at craps 3. From his long experience in casinos, especially as a dealer and boxman, he knew that the vulnerable spots at a dice table were the spots where the players stood closest to the dealers, at both ends. These players could easily get checks handed to them by cheating dealers, particularly when security was lax.

The stickman was being relieved at craps 3, and he tapped his hands together and then showed his open palms to the eye in the sky. This was a strict rule in the casinos, one whose violation could mean dismissal. When a dealer left a table, he had to show that his hands were empty.

Milner stood with Holland and continued to watch the craps game. The table was alive, and the layout was covered with red, green, and black casino checks. The roller was now shaking the dice on the come-out, having just made his previous point. The dice flew across the table and came up ace, ace, snake eyes.

"You know, John," said Milner, "I used to be a craps dealer. I know all the tricks these dealers can pull. They can work out an arrangement to grab checks off the table and hide them, all in one motion, as a team. The stickman is the only one who can see the floormen and boxmen face to face. When their eyes aren't on the table, he can signal with his stick, and all the dealers grab what they can."

"I never saw that happen, Mr. Milner, but it would break the rhythm of the game, and I'm always looking for that change in rhythm."

"Well, keep an eye out for that."

"I sure will."

Milner went over to Moe, who was squatting on the floor, over blackjack 10. Milner watched the game for a few moments. "Moe, who's that player with the stack of blacks and pinks?"

"He's been playing here for a couple of nights. He's a big bettor, Harry, but I don't know who he is."

"Maybe we should ask John." They called him over, but Holland was unable to identify the player.

"That bastard is winning big," said Milner to Moe. "I was watching him earlier."

"Goddamn right he is, Harry."

"Who's watching the play?"

"The floorman, Rogers."

"I'm going to call the floor," Milner said. He got on the phone with the bookkeeper, who sat in the middle of the pit and manned the phones.

"This is Harry Milner. Let me speak to Tim Rogers."

"Yes, Mr. Milner, right away."

Rogers got on.

"Tim, at blackjack 10. You've been watching that game?"

"Yes. You mean at Teddy Butler's table?"

"Is that who's dealing?"

"Yes, Mr. Milner."

"Who's the player with the pinks?"

"Don't know who he is. He's been here a few nights now."

"How's he doing?"

"He's hit us for a bundle. I should say fifteen, twenty grand already tonight."

"And the other nights?"

"I was off last night. You'd have to ask Bert Semple. You want to speak to him?"

"Yes, put him on."

The pitboss picked up the phone.

"Bert?"

"Yes, Harry."

"Bert, at blackjack 10, who's the player there, with the pinks?"

"I was picking up his action for a while. He's been hitting the tables here for the last couple of nights. He must have made over fifty or sixty grand."

"Is he a counter?"

"No. He just bets steady, $500 and $1,000 a hand. He doesn't alter his bets. I don't think he's a counter."

"See if you can find out who he is. And what about the third baseman? He looks like he's winning also."

"Yes, both have been winning. They've been getting the cards, Harry."

"It's more than cards. I was watching them from my office and now I'm in the eye. I don't like the looks of the game."

"What do you think is wrong?"

"I don't know. Go and introduce yourself to the player in the middle. Call me back. I'm on extension 158."

"I'll take care of it right away."

Bert went over to the table. Milner watched him talk to the big player. Then he went to the pit and called up to Harry.

"I introduced myself, but he didn't even give me his name. I asked if he wanted to stay at this hotel, but he said no thanks."

"Keep an eye on that table, Bert."

"Will do," answered the pitboss.

25

Milner had supper at home. Frederica cooked him a simple meal, a steak dinner, and he had a pleasant hour away from the casino. It was hard to drag himself back to his office. When he got there, he reviewed his problems. The Mike English situation yesterday had knocked him out and taken a lot of his time and energy, but perhaps it was behind him now. Perhaps.

A more pressing matter demanded his attention. They had had a poor drop last night and again this evening at blackjack, during the swing shift. It seemed to focus down onto one table, number 10, and two players whipping the El Capitan's ass. Milner switched on the closed-circuit TV and stopped it at blackjack 10.

As he watched, he called the company that serviced the TV system and asked them to send down a video-tape crew that evening. It was short notice, especially on a Saturday night, but they said they'd see what they could do. They'd call back.

He watched the game again, then called the pit and told Semple to change dealers and bring in new cards. Maybe it was the cards. You never could tell. Sometimes the cards ran one way all the time; just a question of their arrangement. That's what he thought happened last night. Anyway, he wanted to have a look at these cards, and asked Semple to bring them to his office.

As he watched, a new dealer, Bill Summers, replaced Butler. And four new packs of cards were put into the game. Summers opened them leisurely, spreading them out and making sure they were all there.

Bert Semple came in a minute later, with the old decks.

"Have you looked at them?" he asked the pitboss.

"No, not yet."

"Leave them here."

He called the floor and had them page Moe Lewis, who picked up the phone at once. Harry told him to come right to his office.

"Moe, these are the cards from blackjack 10. Let's look at them together."

"I was just near the table. We're getting killed."

"What do you think, Moe, you want to bar those two players?"

"I don't know, what do you think, Harry?"

"I have a hunch, Moe, that something's wrong. I just called a TV crew and I want pictures taken of that game. Maybe, if something's wrong, we can spot it and maybe get our money back. If we throw the players out, there it goes. All our money."

"You think we're being cheated?"

"I don't know, Moe. I just have a feeling. You ever get that feeling in your gut?"

"Harry, I'm with you. I know just what you mean."

"Well, let's look these cards over." He grabbed a handful and riffled the backs, to spot any markings. If the cards had been marked, the backs would jump out at you, somewhat like watching a series of cards with continuous-action photographs.

The cards held their pattern. They then examined the fronts and backs carefully, moving them into the light, looking for any kind of indentations or foreign substance on them.

"They're clean," said Milner. "Let's count them." The two men divided them into four decks, two red and two blue.

"It looks like they're all here," said Milner. "I figured maybe they were handmuckers, Moe; adding 10s and aces to the decks. But the decks are clean."

"They look clean to me."

"That's one of the reasons I put four-deck games in," said Milner. "The players never touch the cards. It's a big advantage to us. We cut down the cheats right from the start."

"Harry, what do you think? Maybe they're just holding hot hands."

"It could be, Moe. But I don't know."

"If it's not the cards, what could it be?"

"The dealer."

Moe nodded soberly. "Teddy Butler's been dealing the big games the last week. Also Bill Summers and Lewis Farley."

"Let's watch Bill Summers." They turned their attention to the TV set. Both winners were still at the table: the one betting the pink, or $500, checks and the third baseman, whose bets were more conservative. As they watched, both men won their bets, the third baseman with a blackjack.

"They may be counters," said Moe.

"Bert says no. He says they don't vary their bets the way counters do."

"I hear a whole syndicate out of San Francisco is operating in town," said Moe.

"I heard the same thing. They hit the Sands and the

Frontier, but these guys are not with it. We got the report warning us. Luckily, we didn't get hit."

"We're getting hit now," said Moe.

They kept watching the game, then the phone rang. It was the TV people. A crew was being rounded up; it would soon be on its way.

When the crew came, they were led up to the eye in the sky by Milner. Three cameras were set up to shoot the action from all angles, catching the players and the dealers.

"I want about a half hour film on each of the dealers," said Milner. He called down to the floor and spoke to Bert again.

"Who's been dealing blackjack 10 tonight?"

"Just Butler and Summers."

"OK, relieve Summers now, and in a half hour put him back on the table. Then, Bert, take them both off and shove them on $2 tables. For the rest of the evening."

"There's not that much left tonight."

"Well, whatever time is left. Put in new dealers after each has a half hour."

"Which ones do you want?"

"Anyone that hasn't dealt the $100 tables this week."

"OK. I'll take care of it."

That was all Milner could do for the time being. He went out of the office and onto the casino floor to look the table over, to get a first-hand impression. He had trouble moving freely through the mass of players. All the craps tables were going full blast; the warm bodies were heating up the games.

Summers was still dealing twenty-one at blackjack 10. Teddy was coming out of the coffee shop, having finished his break, and Milner watched him walk through the casino, past the keno lounge toward the pit, adjusting his dealer's apron.

Milner stepped back out of his path, and then, looking

over toward the lounge, he saw Diane. She was talking to a man at the table, his back toward Milner. The man turned around for a few moments, and Milner saw that it was the third baseman at blackjack 10, who also was taking a break from the action.

Diane kissed the man lightly on the lips. *So,* Milner thought, *he must be the one she was talking about . . . Very interesting.* He felt bothered by Diane's involvement with the man. A surge of anger brought color to his face. He watched the player resume his seat at the blackjack table. Milner turned his attention to Diane again. She sat alone at the table with a drink in front of her, staring into space, looking at nothing at all.

Milner walked to the nearest house phone, told the operator to get him the security office. When it answered, Milner asked the chief, Len Bingham, to come down to the floor to see him.

Milner hung up, and continued to watch Diane. A couple of minutes later, Bingham came over to him. He was dressed in street clothes.

"Yes, Mr. Milner?"

"That woman sitting there . . ." He pointed to Diane. "Yes."

"Get her away from the lounge. Get her into your office and question her."

"You want me to arrest her . . . is she a hooker?"

"No. No arrest. Detain her until you get her full name . . . act as if she's a hooker. And find out who she's with here; tell her you want to check it out, otherwise you can't let her go. Then call me in my office while you still have her, and let me know what you found out."

"Right."

He stood back as Bingham walked over to the lounge, to Diane's table. Milner saw Diane look up, startled. Then, after a moment's hesitation, she got up and walked away with Bingham. Milner knew she had no alternative—not as a single woman in a Strip casino.

He stayed out of sight while she was led away toward the security office in the rear of the casino. Milner lit a cigarette and blew out some smoke. There was a bad taste in his mouth. This wasn't his style at all, he thought to himself, not at all, but he had to protect himself.

He returned to his office and sat down. He poured himself a drink. Then he tried the Denver number and slammed down the phone when there was no answer. Damn these bitches. He thought of Diane. She was really good-looking, but good-looking women were a dime a dozen in Vegas. He could be screwing half the showgirls in town if he cared to. It all meant nothing here.

But there was something about Diane. Milner wondered if she was really a hooker. Why was he wondering about her? He tried to recall the night he had spent with her. She was decent enough to him, wasn't she?

Yes, he had to admit that. She was lonely and troubled . . . well, everyone had problems. He had his own problems. He had to protect himself. Milner tried to get her out of his thoughts. He had his own job to think about, his future . . . It all looked unsettled. Anything could happen in the next day or two.

The damned businessmen were coming tomorrow. And he had this problem at blackjack 10. And there was the problem with Mary. And English could act up again. Again, Diane came into his thoughts. Maybe he should have been man enough to leave Diane alone.

Milner poured another drink. His mind seemed jumbled.

The phone rang. It was Bingham.

"I still have her in the other room. Her name is Diane Kimberly. She claims the man she came here with is called Don Steinberg."

"Spell both those names."

Milner wrote them down, and then told Bingham that he could let her go.

"You sure?"

"I told you, let her go, didn't I?" said Milner, his voice rising.

"Yes, sir," was the quiet reply. Milner finished his drink.

26

At blackjack 10, Steinberg sat troubled by Diane's whispered remark. She had told him about being detained, about having to give both of their names to security. She didn't think it had anything to do with his playing, just with her being picked up as a possible hooker. But Diane had really been nervous; she told Don that she was getting right out of the casino and going home.

In Diane's purse was $6,000 of his winnings, which he had given her during the previous break, just in case something happened. When you took the casino this way, you had to get paranoid. Steinberg was tempted to get up now and cash in, just take off and call it a night, but when would he have another night like this? Never. He was really winning this evening—even more than yesterday—but still his wins were nothing compared to those of the other player, the one who knew the signal. That dude was betting the limit, a thousand on each hand, playing two and three hands at a time.

Steinberg continued to mimic the big winner but still couldn't figure out the signal. All night long they had faced two dealers, Bill and Teddy. When Bill was dealing, Steinberg realized that no signal was passed, for the other player would simply play standard blackjack, hitting all bust hands if the dealer showed a 7 or higher, and standing when the dealer showed a bust card himself.

It was Teddy who was giving the signal. He must be a wizard, or doing it electronically, because Steinberg couldn't find it, but somehow it was there, hanging in the air, being transmitted. But what was it? Steinberg would have loved to figure it out, for then, on certain hands where the other player had a pat hand, he would know what to do with his own cards. He had made a few costly mistakes, but that was to be expected in blackjack. You couldn't be a clairvoyant, unless you were getting a signal.

Steinberg knew he had a tremendous advantage over the house, something like 10 percent, and with correct play he was taking them for all he could. He was also counting, thus varying his bets, and with big bets out and knowing whether or not the dealer's card in the hole was a bust card, he was practically coining his own money. He had bet as much as $500 on favorable situations and won most of those big bets.

The cocktail waitress came over and Steinberg ordered a Kahlúa-and-cream, his new blackjack drink. It was soothing to his stomach, which felt ravaged; he had eaten no supper before getting to the tables. He didn't want his stomach doing flipflops, not tonight. The damn tension never stopped, even winning like this.

He knew his play was being watched; he knew security was probably photographing him and getting ready to ask him questions. They had done this to other players . . . When a casino was burned, they took revenge. He'd have to get out of Vegas soon. Damn soon. As soon as possible. He thought of Cape Cod, of the time he had spent there with Paula . . . New England. The sea, autumn leaves, trees and sand dunes and ocean spray. God, he had forgotten what that was all about after his stay in Vegas. It was another world in the East, a world of seasons, of snow and rain, of cloudy days. He'd never thought he'd miss clouds and rainy days as he did now, burned out by the unending brightness of the desert sky. Maybe, he thought, he'd look around for land back East. Land was cheap in upstate New York; maybe a farm, a place of his own finally. With what he had won these last two nights, he was in a position to buy a house and a few acres of land.

His thoughts were interrupted by Teddy, who handed him a red plastic card to insert among the four fresh decks, recently introduced into the game and thoroughly shuffled. He shoved the card into the center of the deck, knowing it made no difference where he put it. Nothing mattered but taking advantage of that signal, that beautiful tell.

The cards were placed in the shoe, and Teddy started dealing. The other player had $1,000 bets on three hands. Steinberg put out $300, and was rewarded with a blackjack. The goddamn cards were perfect tonight.

By the time Teddy took his next break, Steinberg was ahead another $11,000. He cashed in $10,000 more, leaving himself $1,000 to play around with. If he lost this, he was out of the game. Why be greedy? The shift was coming to an end.

He went back to the table to find a completely new dealer there, whose nametag read John. Steinberg put out $200 and lost the hand, then the next hand. He reduced his bet to $100 and then stayed pretty much the same for the next ten minutes. It would soon be time to get out. Steinberg shifted in his seat, and continued to play.

27

The videotape machine was set up in Milner's office, and, as the technician turned it on, blackjack 10 came into focus with Bill Summers dealing.

Milner and Lewis watched the tape in silence as it ran from beginning to end. There was a short pause in the action, and then Teddy Butler began to deal. They watched to the end.

After it was all over, Milner asked Moe Lewis what he thought.

"I think we were taken for about fifteen grand by those two in the hour. Maybe more."

"I mean about the game. Moe, did you see anything wrong with it?"

"Yeah, Harry, something's wrong if they win like that. But I can't put my finger on it."

"I can't put my finger on it either, but the whole game is off. Those two players bet like they were wired to the cards, like they always knew what was going to happen next."

"What do you think it is, Harry?"

"Let's watch about ten minutes more of each dealer."

After watching Summers deal again, Milner stood up and walked around the room, shaking his head.

"As much as I want to find something wrong, Moe, it's just a regular blackjack game. Maybe I was imagining things."

"Like I said, Harry, they just could be holding a hot hand."

"Let's watch the other dealer."

As Teddy dealt, Milner stood by the machine, watching closely. Then he had the machine stopped again.

"Moe, here's where the trouble is. With this dealer. There's something wrong here."

"What do you see?"

"I don't know exactly. Let's watch him together." They watched the full thirty minutes, till their eyes were blurred.

"Moe, I've watched him a few times now on this tape. And you know what's happening? Whenever this bastard peeks at his hole card, the player in the middle never makes a mistake. He never busts, when this dealer has a bust card."

"You sure?"

"See for yourself."

They watched again.

"You're right, Harry."

"But the third baseman sometimes busts. I don't think the third baseman and the other guy are partners. They play two different games. If you ask me, the third baseman's a counter. His bets go up and down."

"Yeah, while the other guy just pours it on. A thou a hand."

"Let's see the second half again," Milner asked the technician.

They watched for several hands, then Milner had the tape stopped.

"I saw something else, Moe. The third baseman is always looking over at the other player's cards. He tries to imitate his play. The other guy never looks at the third baseman at all."

"You're right, Harry, he's too busy looking at the dealer."

"That guy knows what the dealer has in the hole, every time he peeks. I'm sure of it, Moe. He plays like he knows. He doesn't make a mistake. Never makes a mistake. But how does he know?"

Moe lit up his cigar. The room was filled with heavy smoke.

"There's a signal then," said the casino manager.

"Must be. But what kind of signal?"

"Let's watch his hands," said Moe.

"OK."

They studied the tape again.

"It can't be his hands," said Moe. "They're always in the same position."

"What then? The head?"

"Let's watch his head."

The tape began again. Milner glanced quickly at his watch. It was ten after one, and his eyes were watering from the tape and from the smoke. He had smoked almost a whole pack this evening, just watching these lousy tapes, and Moe was puffing on a foul black cigar.

He tried to keep his eyes open. He had to find that signal. He didn't want to drag the dealer in till he had the goods on him. It was there somewhere, because those two players couldn't have that much luck.

They watched fifteen more minutes and had to stop. Moe got into a coughing fit. They opened the door and aired the room out, then called for some coffee and soft drinks.

After they had the drinks and coffee, the tape was started again. It was now one-forty in the morning.

Milner stood close to the set watching. Teddy peeked at his hole card, then turned to look at the first baseman, waiting for the player's decision. The next time he peeked, however, he didn't look up at once. He lingered over the card, ever so slightly, undetectably if not for the videotape.

"Moe, do you see what I see?"

"I don't know, Harry. My eyes are closing on me."

"Moe, look. Watch the way he turns his head on this deal, and watch the way he does it on the next one. He holds it down a couple of seconds longer the second time."

The casino manager rubbed his eyes, then followed Milner's finger as he pointed out the movements on the screen.

"That's some signal," said Moe.

"A beauty. So subtle. It's amazing that a punk like Butler could work out that tell."

They verified it on the screen. Each time Butler lingered on his hole card, it was a bust card.

Milner called the pit and spoke to Bert Semple.

"Bert, where's Teddy Butler?"

"He's dealing at blackjack 4, a $2 table."

"Let him finish off his shift, then bring him in here."

"To your office?"

"Yes. Don't let him get away. You can handle him, can't you, Bert?"

"Are you kidding? Don't worry, Harry, I'll deliver him myself."

"And you can send Bill Summers home. It's Teddy who's ripping us off."

"He'll be in your office. Don't worry."

Milner called the chief of security and had him come to his office immediately. He showed Len Bingham the stopped pictures of Steinberg and Manny Franks on the videotape.

"If they're still in the casino, detain them. That one is named Don Steinberg. See if you can find him. Page him. Do what you can."

After Bingham left, Milner rubbed his eyes, grinding his knuckles into his eyelids. They burned badly. He opened them again, blinked, and reached for the phone.

"I'm calling Tiny," he told Moe.

The casino manager was slumping in a chair, and opened his eyes slowly. "I'm beat, Harry."

"You want to go home?"

"No, not when one of my dealers is fucking me." He stood up and yawned. "I'm going to wash up, Harry."

"Go ahead." Milner dialed Shapiro's number. After eight rings, Shapiro answered in a sleepy voice.

"What's up, Harry?"

"We found a cheating situation here, Tiny. I think we caught the dealer in the act."

"Who was it?"

"Teddy Butler. He deals blackjack on the swing shift."

"How much did he take us for?"

"At least a hundred grand. Just in these last few days."

"Where's the money?"

"I don't know. We'll try and get it back."

"I'm getting up now, Harry. Keep in touch."

"Right."

Milner told the videotape technician to hang around, and he sat down and ordered coffee from the restaurant. He could barely keep his eyes open. Moe came out of the washroom, running his hands through his hair, just as there was a knock on the door.

"Come in," said Milner.

Bert Semple brought in the dealer, Teddy Butler.

28

After another thirty minutes of play, Steinberg realized that Teddy wasn't going to return to the table. He couldn't spot him in the crowded casino, but, taking a break for a couple of moments and walking around, he saw Teddy dealing to a bunch of ladies at a $2 table. They had burned Teddy all right, had gotten wise to him. Steinberg felt it was in his own best interests to cash in and get out right now.

He gathered up the casino checks and walked toward the cashier's cage. It was all over as far as he was concerned. In his hands he held $2,800 more. It had been that kind of night, with good hands being dealt to him continually, the remnants of the fortune that had come his way these last two days.

The big winner at the table was long gone, having done his disappearing act immediately after Teddy took his last break. *That bastard,* thought Steinberg, *must have won at* *least $100,000. Maybe more.* The guy had been on some tear, and the casino would feel the bite of that win.

Steinberg looked at his watch. It was almost midnight. Definitely time to blow this scene, once and for all. He was in view of the cage, and then he stopped suddenly, for before him was a familiar figure. It was Lee Thornton. He couldn't believe his eyes. There he was, big as life. The son of a bitch. Steinberg stuffed the checks into his jacket pocket, and moved back, toward the side exit, where he still had a good view of the cage. He saw Thornton being handed a safe-deposit box, saw him open it and remove some envelopes, then head right for the door he was standing at.

Steinberg moved away, hiding himself in the crowd near the baccarat pit. He watched Thornton go out the side door and head directly for the interior grounds.

Steinberg followed quickly, stepping into the night air. He could see Thornton's tall figure hurrying across the lawn, moving past the pool, heading for the darkened tennis courts. He followed behind, padding softly on the damp grass, unnoticed. Thornton entered a gate leading to the courts, and Steinberg moved faster. Thornton was now in the first court and was leaving through another gate, which led to the rear parking lot of the hotel.

Steinberg began to trot. He got through the parking lot gate and closed the gap on Thornton, who was heading for an isolated car parked near the courts.

Steinberg caught up with him as Thornton was unlocking the front door of the Nova.

"Hey, Lee," he said, standing a few feet behind him.

Thornton wheeled around.

"It's me. Don Steinberg."

Thornton looked at Steinberg, and stood still, the door handle in his left hand. "What do you want?"

"What do you mean, what do I want? You owe me some money, Lee."

"What are you talking about? I don't know what you're talking about."

Thornton crouched to enter the car, but Steinberg pulled the door away from him. "The money," he said.

"I've got to go. I'll call you tomorrow."

Steinberg held the door open, his body blocking Thornton from entering the car.

"I said I'll call you tomorrow," Thornton said. "Now, get out of my way."

"No, we'll talk now."

Thornton suddenly kicked Steinberg in the shin, making him bend over. He kicked him again, but Steinberg got to his feet and managed to grab Thornton by the arm and spin him around, pushing him against the car door.

"That wasn't nice," he said. "You bastard, you cheat me and now you kick me."

"Let go of me. Let go of me, I tell you."

"No way. I want my money now."

They were completely alone in the parking lot, no cars or people nearby. In the distance was the Strip, the traffic a blur of lights and the hum of tires and engines.

"I told you, I'll call you tomorrow and straighten it out."

"No way. Right now." Steinberg still held Lee's arm. "I want my money, my share."

"What share?"

"What share? We had a deal, Lee. I was to get one third of what we won."

"First, get your hands off me."

"No, first I want my money."

"What money?"

"Hey, man, I told you. The money we won at the Hilton."

"What Hilton?"

Steinberg moved closer and pushed his free hand into Thornton's face, pressing his cheeks between his thumb and index finger. Thornton squirmed and squealed with pain.

"Let go."

"All right, but don't fuck with me. I'm not going through this bullshit again. I want my share."

"I hardly won anything that night. Maybe a thousand."

"A thousand? You mean twenty thousand."

"You're crazy."

"Twenty grand. And that's being conservative."

"You're nuts."

"Don't tell me I'm nuts. You son of a bitch, you took off even before I could get an honest count."

"I was sick."

"Sick, shit. You just took off to fuck me out of my share."

The two men stared at each other. Steinberg, though a few inches shorter than Thornton, was considerably broader. His muscles, taut as they were, seemed to be bursting out of his jacket, and his features, so regular when he was relaxed, took on dark overtones, with the broken nose giving him a dangerous look.

"Come on," said Steinberg, "my money. Now."

"I don't have any money with me. It's in the bank. In a safe-deposit box."

"I said, I want it now."

"I can't get it till Monday. Tell me where you'll be and I swear to you, I'll deliver it to you Monday. I swear on my mother's life."

"Are you kidding me? You'll blow out of town now."

"I swear. On my mother's life."

"You son of a bitch," said Steinberg. "You just took

your money out of the safe-deposit box right here at the El Capitan."

Thornton broke the hold, and, in a sudden move, kneed Steinberg, right in the balls. Steinberg doubled up, going to his knees. He caught the point of Thornton's shoe as it went for his eyes and deflected it with one hand. Another kick missed his face, landing on his shoulder.

Steinberg staggered to his feet and planted his forearm against Thornton's neck, forcing his head up and back and moving him against the car. Steinberg's forearm pressed against his adam's apple, causing Thornton to gag and turn purple. Thornton's back bent as the pressure on the neck increased. He slid to the asphalt, his knees touching the ground. Steinberg kept up the pressure, then reached into Thornton's jacket pocket and removed two envelopes. With Thornton on his knees, he released the grip and moved back. Thornton was rubbing his neck with both hands, trying to say something, but all he could do was gasp.

"I'm taking my share," said Steinberg, opening one of the envelopes. He grabbed the money out of it, and began counting.

"Give it back to me," said Thornton, in a choked voice.

"After I get my share." Thornton made a move toward him. "You take one more step and I'll put you away for good," said Steinberg.

"This is robbery."

"Robbery? You robbed me, you prick. I'm taking what's due me."

He counted out fifty $100 bills and threw the half-depleted envelope on the ground, along with the other one.

Thornton picked them up.

"You won't get away with this," he said.

"Don't threaten me, motherfucker."

Thornton's face was pale in the dark night, only the moon's crescent giving off light. "You robbed me. I'll get that money back."

"You fuck around with me," said Steinberg, "and I'll fuck you so bad, you'll wish you never met me." Steinberg turned away and went back through the gate into the tennis courts. He crossed them and went on the lawn, quickening his stride. Near the side door to the casino, he turned to see the Nova's lights on, and the car circling the lot.

After the car was gone, Steinberg went through the casino, headed for the front entrance and his car, parked in the front lot.

Steinberg got into the car. He felt uneasy and had to get out of there right this instant. He zoomed out of the parking space and nearly hit a cab coming in. He hurtled the car through the lot and out into the Strip. At Desert Inn he turned off and drove east, heading for his apartment.

Maybe he was being paranoid, but something was wrong. He could sense it, feel it in his guts. He made a right turn into Paradise Road. Pain was shooting through his groin, through his right leg. That motherfucker had gotten him smack in the balls. Damn, it hurt. He tightened his jaw muscles as another spasm of pain hit him.

That motherfucker, cheating him that way. Taking what was really his. Well, he got it back, and he'd hold onto it, because no one was ever going to take away what was rightfully his. No one.

29

Thornton drove around the Strip aimlessly for half an hour, his whole body shaking with a combination of fear and rage. Twice he had to pull into a side street and park for a few minutes until he regained his composure. He was still shaking as he got out of the Nova at the El Capitan and took the ticket from the parking boy. That bastard, Steinberg, was strong as a bull. When he had that grip on his neck, Thornton thought his blood would stop. *He could have killed me,* Thornton told himself, going into the casino.

In the elevator he realized that his shirt was sticking out of his trousers, and his clothing was in disarray. He pushed the shirt back as best he could, still thinking of that episode in the parking lot. The one good thing was that kick he had gotten in, right in the bastard's balls. He'll remember that shot. But deep down he knew he had been defeated by Steinberg's sheer strength and that he would be no match for him in a real fight.

He walked slowly to his room. His legs were still weak, and he could feel the trembling with every step. Finally, he was at his door, and opened it.

The bed was made and the towels were fresh, but otherwise the room was just as he left it two days before. He took off all his clothes, went into the bathroom, and turned on the shower. He stayed in the shower for a long time, letting the hot water run over his head and body. Leaving the tub, he felt calmer and looked at himself in the large steamy mirror. He was still the same Lee Thornton, and, except for the episode with Steinberg, he looked more relaxed than he had since coming to Vegas.

Thornton brushed his teeth and shaved, glad to be back in his room, so much better than that shithole he had been staying at downtown. Now he didn't have to fear bumping into Steinberg; now he could do as he pleased.

It was an expensive visit, though—$5,000. Thinking of the money, Thornton pulled out the broken envelope and counted the cash. There was $5,100 in it; actually Steinberg had cheated himself of $100. And, Thornton rationalized, if they had split the money at the Hilton, it would have cost him another $3,000. So it turned out OK if he looked at it that way.

Steinberg was lucky, all right. Lucky that this money wasn't really his, and there was no way he could complain about what had happened in the parking lot. Of course, if a security guard had wandered by, he would have made a commotion. But there was no point in complaining to the law, because in the end, he would have to explain more then he cared to explain, and the publicity might reach all the way back to Chicago.

No, he'd let sleeping dogs lie, but if he could figure out a way, he'd get even with that bastard. *Some day,* he thought, *I'll get even with him.*

He put on fresh underwear, another pair of pants, a fresh shirt, and the clean jacket. He changed his shoes and socks. He felt like a new man. By now, the incident that occurred about an hour ago was receding fast, and the night awaited him.

It was amazing, he told himself, that he hadn't gambled all day. Instead, he had returned to see Patti, and had to wait till early in the afternoon before she came back to the trailer park. Thornton had another session with her, paying her $35 this time. But though he lasted longer than he had this morning, in many ways it was less satisfying. He didn't like the idea of paying for a woman, even though she was so much younger, and, after his orgasm, he felt depressed.

After coming, tears had suddenly welled in his eyes, and Thornton was forced to turn his head away from the girl. She sensed that something was the matter, and brought him another of those stupid root beers. It wasn't a soft drink or a hard drink that was going to help; Thornton remembered feeling very depressed, and in that tiny grimy bedroom, all he could think about was his mother, and how ashamed of him she would be if she could see him there.

With all his money in envelopes secreted about his person, Thornton left the room and walked down to the elevator, again a little nervous about the emptiness of the corridor. But his walk and the ride down to the casino were without incident.

Before playing, he decided to have one drink and really relax. He ordered a Drambuie and sat over the liqueur in the lounge, watching the action below him. The casino was still busy, but it had thinned out considerably in the last hour. He glanced at his watch. Five minutes to two.

The shift would end soon, he thought, and the show crowds would be breaking out of the main room. He'd wait till they got out; he didn't want to be in a mob scene on a Saturday night. He had another Drambuie, and the liqueur warmed his insides. Vegas wasn't such a bad place after all, he decided. And he was comfortably ahead. With the big win at the Hilton more than offsetting his earlier losses, and even with Steinberg grabbing that five grand, he still showed a profit of about fifteen grand. Not bad at all.

In fact, if he felt like it, he could take the money and hold onto it, go back to Chicago and practically clear up all his debts, pay back the money to his clients, and wait for another chance to come out here.

He could do that, but of course, he reasoned, he was here now. He had been lucky so far. And he still felt lucky. He could take this money and really roll it up. One good run at any of the games, and he'd be where he wanted to be. He'd be free of Chicago once and for all, free to go anywhere, do anything he wanted. It was a heady dream, all right.

The show crowds broke and the mobs poured through

the casino. Then all receded to normal. Thornton got up and walked down to the tables, rubbing his hands together, looking for the right game. This was going to be his night; he was sure of it.

He decided to play a little blackjack. He had won at the game, but not in this casino, which meant that the El Capitan owed him money. The cards would even out.

He took out a few thousand in cash and started play, but after a few disastrous hands he decided to get up before he really got in deep. Ten minutes of play had cost him $2,000, and he had no confidence in the four-deck game. *Maybe I should stop,* he thought. *Stop playing now, take my profits and go back to Chicago.* He could turn in the car tonight, grab a plane for LA, and call his wife from the airport first thing in the morning, telling her he was on his way home.

Instead, he went to the nearest craps table, wedged his way in, and emptied the remains of the money Steinberg had left in the envelope.

The dice were cold, and before he knew it he had only one black check to show for the entire envelope. After only a little less than an hour's play, he had depleted all that money, the $5,100 that had been bulging in the envelope.

He decided to stop gambling and go back to his room and pack up. But first a drink. He went to the lounge bar and had a vodka tonic, and then another. Yes, he told himself, he could go up to the room now. He was still ahead about ten big ones. He couldn't fault that. It was more in winnings than he had ever held at any time in his gambling career. He had still another vodka and tonic.

From his seat, he could see the baccarat pit at the far end of the casino. A small crowd was watching the play at the table. Thornton decided to watch the game for a little while before returning to his room.

When he got to the pit, he could see why a crowd had

gathered. Mike English, the headliner of the El Capitan show, was sitting in his tuxedo, playing the game. The seat next to the entertainer was open. *Why not,* Thornton told himself, *why not.* He'd risk half an envelope, $5,000 more. If he lost that, back to his room. And if he won, anything could happen.

Thornton entered the pit and sat in seat number 8, right next to the entertainer, who gave him a cursory nod. Lee put $5,000 in cash out in front of him. The El Capitan still used cash in their baccarat game, one of the few casinos that hadn't switched to checks, and it made the game fascinating to the spectators and heart-stopping to the participants. Cash was not abstract, like checks. Checks were just a medium for action. When a player put out a $20 bill, it had value, and he knew what that bill could buy.

The shoe, a wooden device that held all eight decks, so that the players could slip cards out, one at a time, was being held by a Chinese, and the game was stopped for a moment by the callman so that Thornton could get his bet down. He hesitated, and bet $1,000 on Player. He didn't want to pay the 5 percent commission he would have to pay if he bet Bank and won.

English, sitting next to him, also had a large bet out, on Bank.

"Like a drink, sir?" one of the dealers asked him. Like Mike English, he was in a tuxedo. There were three dealers at the table, two handling the commisisons and payoffs, and the third, the callman, who ran the game.

"Yes, thanks." A cocktail waitress materialized immediately.

Meanwhile, the cards were being dealt. The Chinese slid a card out of the shoe toward the callman, then slid one for himself, then another to the callman, and a final card for himself.

The callman took the two cards and, still keeping them face down, flung them to Thornton, who had the biggest bet on Player. These cards were the Player's.

Thornton turned them over quickly—6 and 2, a total of 8, the second-best hand in baccarat.

"Eight, a natural for the Player," said the callman.

The Chinese turned over his cards, jack and 4.

"Four for Bank. Player wins."

The Bank bets were cleared from the table, and ten crisp $100 bills were given to Thornton. He placed the pile of hundreds on his original bet and decided to let the bet ride—$2,000, the maximum bet in baccarat, and the biggest individual bet he had ever made on one hand.

Thornton could feel the excitement of the game. The crowd's eyes were not only on the celebrity sitting next to him but on him. All it took was money, and you were something. He watched English bet two thousand on Bank.

The shoe moved to the next participant, a new man with a clipped mustache which he licked nervously. He had a $100 bet on Bank.

The man holding the shoe slid out the cards. Thornton got the Player's cards again. He turned them over and winced. Ace, king: 1. A terrible hand. He threw them back to the callman, who placed them down in the Player's box in front of him.

"One for the Player."

The man holding the shoe turned his over. A king and queen.

"Zero for the Bank."

Still in business, thought Lee. His heart was pounding under his shirt.

"Card for the Player," the callman ordered.

A card was slid from the shoe face down, and the callman turned it over. It was a queen.

"Still 1 for the Player. Card for the Bank."

Thornton sighed. Any card above an ace beat him, except a 10 or face card, which counted as zero.

The bank's card was a 10.

"Zero for the Bank, 1 for the Player. Player wins."

And, with two hands, Thornton was ahead $3,000.

His drink arrived. He tipped the girl with a dollar bill, wondering if that was enough.

"You really hit it, pal." Thornton turned to see Mike English talking to him.

"Excuse me?"

"I said, you really hit it. What are you betting now?"

"On Player. A thousand."

"I'm with you." The singer counted out a thousand in bills.

The shoe moved to Thornton but he waved it away, and Mike English took it.

"Can't pass up the shoe," he told Thornton, and changed his bet to Bank. He slid out the cards.

The Player's cards were given to Thornton, who turned them over slowly: 7 and 2, a 9, another natural.

"Nine, natural for the Player."

English turned over the Bank's cards. 4 and 3, for a 7. The Player hands won.

"Son of a bitch," said Mike, "I went off a winning bet."

The singer was now down to just a few bills. He asked the dealer for a marker. The dealer looked up at the pit-boss, who sat in a high elevated chair overlooking the game, and was known as a "ladder man." He nodded to the dealer, then put in a call to the cage to verify the singer's credit position.

"How much do you want, Mike?" the dealer asked.

"Ten thousand." The ladder man nodded and English was given his money.

English now followed Thornton's bets, and they won two more bets. Thornton was ahead $8,000.

On the next bet, Lee hesitated. He was thinking of getting up and returning to his room. But how could he leave a winning streak like this? He held $1,000 in his hand, looking at the layout.

"Come on," said Mike English. "Make a bet, pal. I'm with you all the way. You're so lucky, you must have slept with horseshit last night."

Thornton put the money on Bank, and the singer followed his example, betting the $2,000 limit. The Bank hit a natural 8.

"You're a fucking wonder," said English. "What now?"

"Bank again."

This time Bank lost. And from that moment on, the cards turned on Thornton. He kept telling himself to quit with one more losing bet, but he didn't leave the table.

First, the winnings went, all the money he had won at the table. Then the $10,000 he had been ahead before he sat down at the table. Then the contents of one envelope. Then another.

Finally, Thornton was down to his last envelope. He switched his bets back and forth, hunch bets on Bank and Player.

It was five in the morning and he was sweating like a pig, saturated with vodka and tonic, vodka martinis, vodka collinses. Still, his throat felt dry. And his head was bursting with a tension headache as he watched hand after hand lose and thousands of dollars in cash go down the drain.

English was no longer following him, nor even near him. The singer had taken a short break to go to the bathroom and then moved his seat. Right now, the entertainer was winning, and had bought back his last marker.

Thornton had his last bet out, $2,000 on Bank. The Player hand won 7 to 5. It was all over. He was busted.

He got up unsteadily, aware that all eyes were upon

him. He had to grip the side of the table for support. As he did so, he could see English turn his head away.

"Sir," said the dealer, "you have a commission to pay."

"How much?"

"Two hundred dollars."

"Bill me. My room's 3025. Name's Thornton."

He was in a daze.

The pitboss nodded to the dealer.

"We'll bill you. And better luck next time."

What next time? Thornton asked himself. He had just dropped $65,000 at this table.

Somehow he got to his room, and flung himself on the bed, fully clothed. What had he done? What had he gone and done? Dropped all his money, all his clients' money. He was busted, finished.

Oh, God, he asked himself, was this a dream? Had it really happened? Would he wake up tomorrow to find this was just a nightmare?

He was sick to his stomach, and went to the bathroom, trying to vomit. He gagged and drooled, but nothing happened.

How could he go through this night? How could he wake up tomorrow and face his life? What was going to happen to him? He couldn't return to Chicago now. Disbarment, disgrace, maybe even prison.

He thought of all the times he could have left the table. When he was winning, he could have left, when he was even, there were so many times. If only he could relive those last few hours—but that was impossible.

Thornton sat at the edge of his bed, his head in his hands. His head was ice cold and covered with perspiration and his hands were sweaty.

He just couldn't go on like this. He couldn't. What could he do?

Thornton thought of the hooker, Patti. When he was over there that afternoon, again she had offered to sell him that gun, this time for $50. He rummaged through his pockets, throwing away the empty envelopes. He got out his wallet, and counted the cash in there: $96. Not even enough to fly home with. Barely enough to pay the balance of the rental on the car. He went into the bathroom and rubbed his face and hair with a towel, trying to get rid of the sweat. Then he readjusted his clothing. He looked like hell.

Thornton left the room and went downstairs. He got his car from the parking-lot boy and headed east, toward Boulder Highway.

30

"Sit down, Teddy," said Harry Milner, pointing to an empty chair near his desk. The dealer saw Moe Lewis staring at him and remained standing.

"Go ahead, sit down."

"What's this all about?"

"Don't you know?"

"Know what?"

The dealer told himself, *Hold on, don't blow this.* But it was tough being in this office with the big studs of the El Capitan. *You're in deep,* he told himself. He prayed that Manny Franks had left the casino, because without him, there was nothing they could do. It was their word against his. That's what it boiled down to, their word against his.

He sat down, crossing and uncrossing his legs. He should have known something was wrong, because of what was happening tonight. There was so much activity around the table, so many eyes watching the play. But it was going to be the last night they pulled the scam, and he knew if he got through it, he was set for life.

Still, he could have been more cautious, Teddy told himself. He could always tell when they were watching him from the eye in the sky, because the chandeliers in the casino would shake when men were up there. Tonight they shook plenty, but he hadn't paid that much attention. All he could think of was that Manny Franks was winning thousands, and half of it belonged to him.

He took a cigarette from Milner, even though he hardly ever smoked anything but pot. It was something to do, holding the smoke, a buffer between him and the hotel president.

"Do you know who I am?" Milner asked him.

"Yes sir, you're Mr. Milner."

"And do you know my position here?"

"Yes sir. You're the head of the hotel."

"Teddy, how long have you worked for the El Capitan?"

"Three years now."

"All the time as a blackjack dealer?"

Milner's voice was soft and gentle. Teddy told himself, *It's a trap, be cool.*

"Yes sir."

"You work any other shifts besides swing?"

"When I first came here, I was on graveyard. For about two years. Then they moved me to swing."

"How much do you make?"

"Uh . . . $28 a day."

"Plus tokes."

"Yes, plus tokes." He tried to force a smile, but couldn't manage one. He puffed on the cigarette and blew out smoke without inhaling. If he could only get out of here, get to his place, see Manny Franks this morning . . . collect his money. Jesus, if he could do that, he'd take the first plane out of town, to anywhere.

"Teddy, you make a good living here, don't you?"

"It's all right. Yes, it's a good living."

"Any complaints?"

"No."

"Your table has taken a beating the last few nights. You know that?"

"Well, Mr. Milner, the cards have been bad for me. I busted a lot of hands."

"Those things happen, don't they?"

"Yes sir."

"How much did those two players make the last few nights?"

"Which two?"

"The one who sat in the middle of your table tonight, with the long brown hair . . . wearing that flowered shirt . . . the one betting those pink checks."

"Him?"

"And the third baseman. They've both been playing at your table for three days now."

"No, they haven't."

"They haven't?"

"No." He was finished with the cigarette and got out of the chair to grind it out on the desk's ashtray.

"How long have they been playing at your table?"

"Who?"

"Let's take the third baseman."

"Him? I don't know. The last two nights."

"And the other one?"

"Three nights."

"You know the third baseman?"

"No."

"The other one?"

"No." He shook his head emphatically to underline the answer.

"They know you, Teddy?"

"They might know my name. I got my name on my tag."

Milner lit a cigarette and stepped back. The silence hung heavily in the room. Moe Lewis hadn't taken his eyes off the dealer, eyes that burned with hate. Moe was the wrong guy for a dealer to burn. Milner shuffled through some papers on his desk, looking up to see Teddy fidgeting in his chair, crossing his legs, then leaning forward.

"Do you know how much those two took from us these last few days, Teddy?" he asked.

"No sir."

"And all from your table?"

"It's not my table, Mr. Milner. You keep calling it my table, but other dealers deal at the table."

Milner disregarded the explanation. "Those two took us for about a hundred twenty grand. That's a big loss for us. A very big loss."

Milner stood up and leaned against the wall behind his desk, standing beneath the clock. "You know something, Teddy, I've been in the gambling business a long time. So has Moe Lewis. We know what this business is all about. Sometimes we take a beating, but we're in it to make money. We all make money—the casino, the executives, the dealers. We all make a good living from the gambling business." He coughed and continued. "But sometimes the casino loses. That's the nature of the business. You can't win all the time. This isn't a grocery store where you buy something for a quarter and sell it for thirty cents. Here, we have an advantage, and we hope that advantage holds up. Do you understand that?"

"Yes sir."

"We know a dice table gets cold for us and hot for the players, or a blackjack table goes bad for a while. A player gets a hot hand and kills us. This has happened before and it will happen again. You understand?"

"Yes."

"We don't mind a loss, but what we do mind is being cheated. We don't like to be cheated, Teddy. And especially by our own people." He let the words hang in the air, his voice still low and soft.

Butler could feel the sweat running down his sides. He was thirsty as hell. He asked for a glass of water.

"The water cooler is against the wall. Get some if you want."

Butler got up and filled a paper cup with water. He drank four cupfuls, then squashed the cup and dropped it into the wastebasket. He stood near the cooler and stretched.

"Sit down," he was told.

"Mr. Milner, what's this all about?"

"Sit down."

Butler sat down again.

"We have dealers with us for fifteen, twenty years. We're loyal to our people, and we expect the same loyalty. And we deal an honest game here, Teddy. All these hack writers write about Vegas and how the casinos cheat the players. You know better, Teddy. We don't cheat them; we worry about them cheating us. But we don't expect our own people to cheat us. No, Teddy, we don't expect that." Milner coughed again, a harsh, hacking cough. "I'll get to the point, Teddy. You've been cheating us."

"No. No, Mr. Milner."

"We just found out about it a couple of days ago, but we think you've been cheating us for a long time now."

"No, that's not so."

"You've been signaling your hole card to the players. They killed us at your table because of your tell."

"No."

"Teddy, we have the proof."

He told the dealer to turn around and the technician turned on the videotape machine. The dealer's heart jumped a beat as he watched himself on the screen.

"We know your signal, Teddy. It's done with your head."

"No."

The set was turned off.

"You fucking punk," said Moe Lewis. "We ought to take you out to the desert and leave you there."

The dealer took a deep breath, and crossed his legs again, then uncrossed them.

"Who was that player you worked with?" Lewis asked.

"I didn't work with a player."

"Who's the other guy, the third baseman?"

"I don't know."

"You're a fucking liar," said Lewis.

"No."

Milner interrupted, holding up his hands to Moe. "Teddy, we already know the name of the third baseman. It's Don Steinberg. What arrangement did you make with him?"

"I didn't make any deal. I never saw him before in my life."

"And the other player. What's his name?"

"I don't know him either."

"Look, Teddy, once we get our money back, we won't hold you any more. You can take off. You won't work again in Nevada, but we won't turn you into the law. That's my deal, if you cooperate with us, and tell us who that big player was and where the money is."

The dealer shook his head.

"I'll give you a minute to make up your mind."

He looked at his watch.

"Well?" Milner asked.

The dealer shook his head again.

Milner opened the door and told a security guard outside to come into the office. Then he motioned for Moe Lewis to join him in the hallway.

"You're being too easy," the casino manager told him. "This bastard needs a lesson."

"Screw the lesson. If we get the money back, that's all I care about. What are we going to do, take him to court?" He coughed harshly. "Show a goddamn jury the fucking film? In this town, they never convict anyway. They say, fuck the casinos. The locals are all losers at the casinos, Moe."

"Why don't you call Tiny again?" asked Moe. "Let him handle it."

"I don't like what he's going to do, Moe."

"Hey, what difference does it make? You did all you could with the fucker. Let him handle it."

"You mean with Augie Panetta?"

Moe stared at his boss. "Let it go out of our hands, Harry. Let him take care of it. He'll know how."

"Moe, this isn't the old days. I don't want a dead dealer on my conscience. Or one missing both his hands." Milner closed his eyes. If only he could go to sleep, get away now. But he had to face this. "Moe, go back to my office. I'll be there in a minute." Milner went to his secretary's desk and sat down in her vacant chair. He had tried, he told himself, he had done all he could.

He called Tiny Shapiro and told him all that had happened.

"Bring him over here, Harry."

"I'm not taking him over."

"Harry, you don't have to bring him over. Just send him over."

"Tiny, what are you going to do with him?"

"Harry, that fuck stole our money. After you called, I got in touch with Mr. B. He's very concerned about this. We want our money back."

"I know that, Tiny."

"Look, Harry, if you're not sending him over here, we'll come and get him."

"Tiny—"

"Harry, as of right now, it's out of your hands. You understand? We'll be right over."

Milner went back to his office. He told the videotape technician he was free to go. Then he sat down at his desk again, his head in his hands. Finally, he looked up. Moe was sitting in a chair, his head bowed, his eyes closed. Only the security guard and the dealer were awake and alert.

"Why do I have to stay here?" Butler asked Milner.

"You just sit there."

"Why? Why can't I go home now?"

"Are you kidding?"

"What's going to happen?" the dealer asked.

Milner didn't answer.

"Can I see you outside for another minute?" Moe asked Milner.

"Sure." They stepped out again.

"Did you speak to Tiny?" Moe asked.

"Yeah, he's on his way over here now."

"Who's this guy, Steinberg?"

"I found out about him through security."

"Tiny will take care of him."

"I'd rather handle it myself."

"Don't be crazy, Harry. Let Tiny handle it."

"He didn't take us for that much."

"Hey, Harry, what's with you? Tiny will want to handle it. Let him . . ."

As they waited in the corridor, Shapiro came in. He shook hands with Lewis and Milner, and then went into the office with them to see Butler.

"Is this the punk?" Shapiro asked.

"That's him," said Moe. "Tiny, we got the name of one of the players. Don Steinberg."

Milner looked over sharply at Moe, but the casino manager didn't flinch.

"What's the other guy's name?"

"He won't say," said Moe.

Shapiro looked down at the dealer. "Who's the other guy, punk?"

The dealer shook his head.

"OK, punk, on your feet."

The security guard jerked Teddy out of the chair and held his arm as he escorted him out of the office. The other men followed, walking behind the dealer and the guard.

In the rear lot, a car was waiting, its engine on, the lights shining, and the exhaust milky white in the early morning air.

"Leon's driving," said Shapiro, as they stopped ten feet from the car.

"Who's in the back seat?" Milner asked, squinting his eyes and bending down to get a better look.

"Someone," said Shapiro. "It's out of your hands now, Harry."

Butler was pushed into the car by the guard, and Shapiro got in after the dealer, wedging him into the middle of the rear seat. Shapiro waved and the car took off.

"Who was that in the car?" Milner asked Lewis as the car circled around and headed for the Strip.

"Augie Panetta."

"Jesus."

"Forget about it, Harry. We did what we could. You can bet your bottom dollar they'll get the money back."

"I'm not worried about the money, Moe. For God's sake, you think that's all that's on my mind, the fucking money?"

He turned abruptly and walked away from the casino manager, his fists clenched, his head about to explode.

31

They were sitting in Diane's living room. Steinberg had his shoes off, his jacket on a chair, his casino checks and cash piled on the coffee table.

The casino checks added up to $2,800. All his cash was in two identical stacks, and it totaled $22,000. This included the $5,000 he had taken from Thornton. He had won enough money in two nights for his stake, for his ticket out of Vegas.

"That money looks good," said Diane.

"It sure the fuck does," Steinberg agreed. He bent over and fondled the casino checks, all El Capitan blacks, and then shoved them over toward Diane.

"Here, baby, this is yours."

"Mine? What are you talking about?"

"Shit, Diane, if you didn't introduce me to that bastard, Thornton, I'd never have made this bread. He was the one got me turned on to the scam. Go on, take it."

"You're crazy, you know that?"

"Yes, I know it. But I'm blowing this town, baby. Blowing it for good."

"How about some music?" he asked Diane.

"OK. What do you want to hear?"

"You put it on."

She got up, barefoot and wearing her blue nightgown, went to the record stack. She looked over the discs and put a record on the turntable. *Chicago* blasted out at them.

"I like that record, Don."

"Yes."

He got up and stretched, and then went into the kitchen.

"What do you want, Don?"

"Something to drink. You got any bourbon?"

She got up and looked through the closets, but couldn't find any. He settled for rye, drinking it straight.

The music came on strong. The phone rang, then the answering machine snapped into place.

"One of my many lovers," Diane said. She lit a cigarette and put her head back, blowing out the smoke slowly. "When are you going to leave?

"What?"

"When are you going to leave?"

"I don't know. Anytime. Maybe tomorrow."

Diane pressed her feet against the casino checks, moving them around with her toes.

"Where are you going?" she asked.

"I don't know yet. I'm keeping things open. Maybe go east."

"Why don't I cash these in tomorrow, Don? Then you and me, we could go somewhere. We could go east together and then maybe fly to Europe. Get our passports in New York."

He poured another drink but didn't say anything.

"What do you say?"

He still didn't answer. She looked quickly at him, then

looked away, and followed the smoke trailing from her cigarette with her eyes.

"And when we get back," Diane continued, "I could pick up my kid, or have him come live with me . . . with us. We could try it out, see how it worked out."

"I don't know." He coughed, and gulped down the rest of the drink. He felt clammy.

"I'm going to take a shower," Steinberg said.

"Go ahead."

He went into the bathroom and pulled off his clothes, which were still damp with perspiration. He stepped into the shower. Later he dried himself with one of the big yellow towels initialed DJK, and with the towel draped around his waist, left the bathroom.

Diane stared at him. "You look lovely in yellow," she said.

Steinberg sat down in a chair opposite the couch.

"Yeah, I feel better now. What time is it?"

"Ten after four."

"I'm going to think over what you said." He yawned. "I'm so beat now, I can't think straight."

"It might be nice, just the two of us."

"I just don't know. I want to get some land in the East. Then maybe . . . I don't know. Maybe it would be better if I went alone, found something. Then you could come and visit me. We could spend some time together and see what happened."

He went into the kitchen and poured another drink for himself. He was both wired and exhausted, all at once, a strange sensation.

"You could visit me," he continued. "Then we could see how things went. I just can't see flying to Europe now. Just can't. I have to find a place for myself. You understand?"

She didn't answer.

"You understand?"

"Sure," she said, finally. "I understand."

"I think I'm going to get dressed and take off."

"Sure," she said, "you do that."

Sunday

32

The ringing of the phone jolted Steinberg awake. It was daylight, and the sun was casting long white stripes across the bedroom. Steinberg picked the phone up, cleared his throat, and said hello.

"Hello, is this Steinberg? Don Steinberg?"

"Yes." He didn't recognize the voice at all.

"My name's Tom Durham."

"Who?"

"Tom Durham."

By this time Steinberg was wide awake, a habit he had acquired in Nam: immediate awareness after being shaken awake. "Do I know you?" Steinberg asked.

"No. I work for Mr. Milner at the El Capitan. He'd like to see you this morning."

Steinberg said nothing. He looked around the room, and saw the two envelopes stuffed with cash that he had left on the dresser, each bound in heavy rubber bands. "Who's Milner?"

"Mr. Milner is president of the El Capitan, and he asked me to pick you up and take you to his home."

"What's this about?"

"He said you'd probably know, but, in any event, he said he'd discuss it with you when you got there."

"When does he want to see me?"

"Right now, if possible. In fact, I'm calling from around the corner to your apartment. I'm at the Stop and Go on Twain."

What was this all about? Steinberg tried to think . . . was he being suckered into something? Jesus, he didn't know.

"Give me your number, and I'll call you right back," he told Durham.

"Look, Steinberg, it's best if you come with me to Mr. Milner's house."

"I'll call you back."

"Whatever you want. I'll wait here for no more than five minutes." He gave Steinberg the number and hung up.

Steinberg was immediately out of bed, on his feet, throwing cold water on his face to make himself really alert. Jesus, guys from the El Capitan. They were after him; he had to get out of here. Then he wondered why they were calling. If they wanted him that bad, they could just come in and take him. In this town, half the security guards in the casinos were deputized. Anyway, the cops were very cooperative when it came to Strip hotels.

He went to the front window, and peeked out. There were two empty cars parked outside. Maybe he was just getting paranoid again, but why would they want him now, except for what happened there the last two nights?

They wanted their money back. No way. He got dressed and put on his best jacket, stuffing it with his cash. He'd have to be crazy to leave it in this place. Then he might as well kiss it goodbye.

There was a knock on the door.

Steinberg decided to ignore it, but the knocking continued.

"Who's there?" he finally asked.

"Tom Durham."

"What do you want?"

"I want to speak to you."

Steinberg went to the window and looked out. There was only one man on the entrance balcony. He opened the door slightly.

"Look," said Durham, "it's in your best interests to come with me to Mr. Milner's house."

"Why?"

"I can't really answer that question. I don't know what this whole thing is about, but I can tell you this . . . there are two deputy sheriffs in a car downstairs."

"You're bluffing."

"Take a look."

"I already looked."

"Well, they're parked on this side of the street. If you want to see them, lean over the railing."

"You wait here."

"Sure. Take a look."

Steinberg bent over and saw a car manned by two men in uniform. The car was unmarked, but he could see a badge on one of the men. They sat and waited, with the motor running.

"Satisfied?"

"What's this about?"

"Look, Steinberg, I'll be frank with you. I don't know. Milner wants me to drive you over to his place. That's all. You talk to him there."

"And if I don't?"

"You'll be detained by the sheriffs."

"For what?"

"I don't know. That's between Milner and you."

Durham drove a gray Datsun 26oZ, and Steinberg sat silently beside him in the front seat as they headed down

Karen to Milner's place. Behind him, he was sure, the white car with the sheriffs was following, but he decided to act cool and not look in the rear-view mirror or turn his head. He had the money with him. He'd see what would happen.

When they got to Milner's house, a black housekeeper answered the door and told both men to come in.

Milner was already dressed and waiting. He said hello to Durham and then introduced himself to Steinberg with a handshake. Then he told Durham to wait outside in the car.

"Come on in," he told Steinberg. "How about some coffee?" He led Steinberg into the dining room.

"OK."

"Sit down. Relax."

Steinberg sat on one of the dining-room chairs, stretching his legs. He still had a headache from the tension of the night before.

"So you're Don Steinberg?"

"That's right."

"You're a local, aren't you?"

"In a way."

"How long have you lived in Vegas?"

"Eight months."

"That's not long. How do you like it?"

Steinberg shrugged. He watched the maid bring out a pot of coffee, some cups, and a plateful of toast.

Milner poured out two cups of coffee, sliding one to Steinberg. He moved over the creamer and the bowl of sugar.

Steinberg shook his head. He took a piece of toast and chewed it, they drank some of the strong black coffee.

"So," said Milner, "I guess you know why you're here."

Steinberg didn't answer.

"You know, don't you?"

"Maybe."

"It's about your prowess at our twenty-one tables. You really gave them a beating these last two nights."

Steinberg chewed on the crust of the toast.

"How much did you win?"

Steinberg shrugged.

"We figure about twenty thousand. That's pretty close to the actual amount, isn't it?"

Steinberg said nothing.

"I enjoy one-sided conversations," said Milner. "Really enjoy talking to myself."

"What do you want me to say? Get to the point."

"All right, let's get to the point, Don. You don't mind me calling you Don, do you?"

"No. Whatever you want."

"Don, there was a bad situation at that table you were playing at. We had a dealer cheating us, and you were in on it. That's the point."

Milner stared at the silent Steinberg.

"Any comment?" Milner asked.

"No."

"Well, that's it in a nutshell. We got taken by you and another guy. We've already gone after the other player. We'll get our money back from him. And now we want our money back from you."

"For what?"

"For cheating us."

"I didn't cheat you."

"Well, I don't want to get into the fine points of cheating. You knew a signal was being passed and you took advantage of it. Don't you call that cheating?"

"No. I could have lost as well as won."

"That's so, but not likely. If you lost, we wouldn't be having this little talk. But the thing is, you won. You want more coffee?"

"No."

"Yes, the point is, you won."

"What does whatever I won mean to your casino? What difference does it make to the El Capitan?"

"It's nothing, really. Really and truly, it's just peanuts. But that's not the point at all. The thing is, we were hustled. Now, I'm a little disturbed by it, but I have men—point owners in the casino—who are not only disturbed but angry. And in this town, you don't want to have point owners angry at you. It's not healthy."

"Is that a threat?"

"No, of course not. Personally, I don't give a damn. I'm looking at you and figuring, if you're stupid, you'll piss it all away at the tables, and if you're smart, you'll blow out of town today or tomorrow with your winnings. And I think you're smart."

Steinberg said nothing. He watched Milner light a cigarette.

"You're probably wondering," said Milner, blowing out some smoke. "why the president of a Strip hotel is bothering with you right now. Why you weren't just arrested and brought down to the hotel. Right?"

Steinberg didn't answer.

"It's just a matter of style, Don. I wanted to see you and talk to you. In fact, if you want, you can take off, get out of here, drive out of town, or take a cab to the airport. You'd be gone and off my hands, and I'd even wish you good luck." He paused. "Because you'd need it."

Steinberg was leaning back, listening soberly.

"You'd need good luck, believe me. I'm telling you this for your own good. First, you may or may not be able to get out of town. I wouldn't be surprised if there weren't a few men waiting for you right now in your apartment."

"You sent them there?"

"Hell, no. In fact, I did you a big favor in getting you out of there, and over here. These men . . . you're screwing around with a Strip hotel, Don. I may be president, but there are some people connected with the owners I can't control. And they know who you are and want their money back. That's it. They're going to get it back, too. Let me tell you that. They'll get it back whether it means finding you in Vegas or in Oshkosh or in New York or wherever. They'll find you one day, and they'll get that money back. And they'll get you as well."

Steinberg watched Milner's eyes.

"In fact, Don, if they find you here in Vegas, I can't say what will happen."

"You're talking in riddles," said Steinberg. "You tell me you have no control over them, and with the other side of your mouth, you're laying a whole bunch of heavy threats on me."

"I only have one control, Don. I can make a call. I can call and say you returned the money. That it was done friendly, and that's that. That'll be the end of it. Or you can take your chances; that's what I'm saying."

"It's my money. I won it."

"You won it because of a cheating situation. I could argue with you about it all day, but I don't have the time. And frankly I don't care. I'm laying down the facts to you. You can do what you want."

"I want to keep the money. Fair enough?"

"That's up to you. I'll have Tom drive you back to your place."

"Maybe I'll take a cab."

"Or get a cab. I don't care once you leave here."

Steinberg stood up.

"But, Don," said Milner, "I wasn't bullshitting you. I could name some names . . . Anyway, leaving isn't going to be so simple."

Steinberg stared down at Milner, who was still seated, lighting another cigarette.

"Take your friend, Diane."

Steinberg stood still.

"She's going to remain in town. Going to send for her kid. She wants to have a life here. But I'll tell you something . . . The next time she shows up in any Strip hotel, whether she's alone or with a guy or girl, she'll get busted as a hooker. We have an easygoing casino, but others aren't like us. She won't last two weeks in this town. What'll happen is she'll wind up doing time if the casinos put some pressure on the courts. And they can, believe me. And she's got a kid; you have to think about that."

Steinberg didn't move. His face took on a sneer.

"What you're telling me, Milner, is if you can't get to me, you'll get to Diane."

"Me? I don't want to get to anyone. I'm just telling you the score. That's the score in Vegas."

Steinberg didn't move.

"Look," said Milner. "I'll be reasonable with you. Don't give me all the money back. Keep a couple of grand for yourself, for your time and trouble. And as you said, you could have lost." Milner blew out some smoke. "Well," he said, "look, Don, let's end this charade, OK? If I guess right, you have the money with you, in your jacket pockets. So, why not be reasonable?"

"You keep talking about how you're doing this for me . . ." said Steinberg. "But Milner, you're just a son of a bitch in your heart, you know that. You're just like all the other scum in Vegas."

"Hey, look, let's not get personal, OK?"

"No, we won't get personal. All right, I have the money, but it's not all El Capitan money. Five grand is mine."

Milner smiled.

"Keep smiling," said Steinberg, "and I walk out the

232

door, and if your boys try to stop me, I'll take you with me."

"Now, look . . ."

"No," said Steinberg, "you look. You put a heavy threat on me. It doesn't work. You put it on Diane. OK. I'll give you your money, but not my money. Now, five grand is mine. And I'm going to take two more off the top, with your money."

"OK."

Steinberg took out the envelopes and counted out seven thousand quickly, racing the bills through his fingers. He divided the seven thousand into two piles, and placed rubberbands around each one. The smaller pile, containing two thousand, he stuck into his trousers; the other, into his jacket pocket.

"You want to count it first?" he asked Milner, as he stuck the money into his clothing.

"No. I'll take your word for it."

"Count the rest," he told Milner. "And I want a receipt for it."

"Sure."

"And I want proof that you're who you say you are."

"Why not?"

Milner sat and counted the money, added it up one more time, then wrote down the amount, and signed his name to a receipt.

"That receipt just shows how much there is," he told Steinberg. "It doesn't mean it belongs to you anymore."

"I know that."

"Well," he told Steinberg, "I think you did the right thing. You ended it cleanly. Yes, you did the right thing. The smart thing."

He looked up at Steinberg, seeing only scorn on the other man's face.

33

By the time Thornton left the trailer park, it was late morning, and the sun was climbing high into the sky, giving off tremendous heat. He felt sweaty from his sleepless night, and, he could barely keep his eyes open as he drove the rented car back to the El Capitan.

Thornton parked on the side of the hotel, avoiding even the small tip he'd have to give the valet parking boys, and went up to his room. He took off his clothes, took a hot shower, and lay down on the bed again, hoping for sleep.

But sleep wouldn't come. Time ticked away. He lay in bed, shutting his eyes, opening them again. He was utterly drained, and worse, depressed by the events of the previous night.

The whole ordeal with the prostitute, Patti, had been tiring, too. They had haggled and haggled, both of them tired and unkempt. She had been out drinking the night before and was hung over. Finally, after almost an hour's arguing back and forth, he got the gun for $45. It was a bargain, he guessed, since she was desperate for money.

Patti said her rent was overdue, and she pleaded with him for extra money, or to at least have a session in bed with her. She'd only charge him $15, but he turned her down.

Well, he thought, lying on the bed in the semi-darkened room, *at least I have the gun.* It was in his jacket pocket, black and bulky. He had never fired a gun and Patti had to show him how it was done, and how bullets were loaded into chambers.

Sleep was impossible. He kept thinking of his family in Chicago, of his clients, of all the bad news that was awaiting him. What was he going to do? He couldn't return and he had no money. He was down to about $50 and even the thought of spending money on meals worried him. He couldn't afford to spend any money at all.

There was just one thing to do, he thought—disappear. Disappear and start a new life somewhere. A few hours before, in the flush of his victory at baccarat, that thought would have been enchanting. He had sixty or seventy thousand dollars, money enough for ten years in a place like Mexico. Now he had just enough for two days in America.

There was still a good part of the car rental to be paid, gas to be put into the Nova, a bill for his commissions here at baccarat. At least his room was paid up.

But what did it all matter? He remembered reading somewhere that men got the lives they deserved. When he read that statement, he had been shocked at its truth. Because it was so true of his life. His involvement with his wife's family, his dull profession, everything he had done since he was a youth had been wasted. All wasted. A penny-ante life. What had he to show for it all but debts? He didn't have anything left, not even credit cards. They had been taken away by the companies years ago, when he ran up huge bills and lost it all at Arlington Park.

Thornton struggled to his feet. He got dressed again and looked around the room. He had to get out of here, out of Vegas. He threw his things hurriedly into the suitcase. At least he had a car waiting. He'd dump it in California after he had made good use of it, and then call in and tell the car-rental people it was stolen. He could always do that. What he needed right now was money, cash. That's what he needed, cash to get going, to get out of Vegas. He couldn't leave without money.

Thornton's thoughts were on Steinberg. The bastard had robbed him of the $5,000—money that was rightfully his. He was nothing but a thief, robbing him that way. He could feel himself red in the face, burning with the thought of that $5,000. If he had it now, he could get out of town, move somewhere in California, work his way to a good life.

Thornton left the room, carrying the small bag. He walked down the corridor and waited for the elevator. The corridor was empty. Sunday morning. He waited patiently for the elevator, then took it down to the lobby floor, and walked into the casino. It was slow, but there was still action. A craps table was going at full tilt, and the men were screaming after a point was made.

Thornton hurried through the casino. It had been his burial place the night before, and the sooner he got out of the El Capitan, the better. He walked across the lawn to the side gate, which led to the parking lot where his car was waiting. Near the tennis courts there was a public phone, and putting down his bag, Thornton looked up Steinberg's number and called him. There was no answer.

That didn't mean anything, he figured; he might be sound asleep or not answering his phone. Or at the tables somewhere, or with a girl. Thornton copied down Steinberg's address, a place on Royal Crest, wherever that was. Well, it wouldn't be hard to find. He got to his car and drove out of the lot, heading up the Strip.

Pulling into the first gas station, he asked the attendant where Royal Crest was. The boy didn't know but directed him to a map in his office.

Thornton looked it up, near Twain, between Paradise and Maryland Parkway. Not far at all. He got back into the Nova, noting that the fuel gauge was almost empty. Well, he couldn't afford gas right now. He couldn't afford anything right now. What he needed was that $5,000 back from Steinberg. Then he'd be in business.

As he approached Royal Crest, Thornton had second thoughts. What he was planning to do—take that $5,000 from Steinberg—was just the same as robbery. It was the classic definition of robbery—taking money by threat or force. But it was his own money he was after. That wasn't robbery. The fine distinctions of law were lost in the crevices of his tired brain. He needed money, and he had the gun.

His nerves grew taut as he turned the car into Royal Crest. God, he thought, it was just like playing craps; the same excitement, the same dread of something going wrong, and the same anticipation of getting money, big money. He could feel his heart thudding, and his hands were shaking as he slowly cruised down the street, looking for the right address. There it was, a motel-type apartment building, two stories, open stairways leading to the second floor.

Thornton parked the car and got out. The gun was in the side pocket of his jacket; it bulged and weighed the jacket down. He walked slowly across the street, an inner voice telling him this was his last chance to back down, to stop this madness.

But drowning that voice was the thought of $5,000. With that money, he wouldn't have to return to Chicago, wouldn't have to face the family, the disbarment, all that went with it. This was his easy way out, a way out to California, to sunny skies and easy living, all within easy reach of the casinos of Las Vegas.

He went to the mailboxes and looked up Steinberg's apartment. Number 23. The second floor. Thornton went up the concrete steps, feeling them rumble under his weight. He climbed, feeling as though he was now outside his body, as though he were a cameraman recording his own progress up the stairs.

Number 23 was three doors down from the south end of the building. The door was closed, and it was difficult to tell if the lights were on because of the sun hitting the closed drapes. Thornton knocked on the door, very lightly. There was no answer.

He knocked again, a little harder, rapping his knuckles against the painted wood. No answer. He turned the handle. Surprisingly, the door was unlocked. He pushed it open slowly.

The place was a shambles. He stepped inside, closing the door behind him. The furniture was overturned and ripped apart, and as he went into the back bedroom, he could see that the closets and dresser drawers were emptied out, the mattress sliced open and stacked against the wall. He didn't know what to think.

Thornton stepped over broken glass, looking down at a woman's face in a photograph. It smiled up at him. He grimaced and went back into the living room. He didn't know whether to leave, whether to stay and wait for Steinberg, or just get out of here.

He picked up an overturned kitchen chair and sat down. His tired brain tried to think. What should he do?

He lifted his head abruptly as footsteps sounded on the balcony outside. He took the gun out with cold shaking fingers, holding it tightly in his right hand. And waited.

He heard a key put into the lock. Then the door opened and Steinberg stepped in. Steinberg hesitated, looking at the chaos in the room, and then he saw Thornton with the gun.

"Did you do this, motherfucker?" he asked Thornton.

"No, I just got here. Close the door."

"Close it yourself, you prick."

"You close it."

Steinberg left it open, and walked into the bedroom, past Thornton. He picked up Paula's picture and came out with it again.

"Did you do this?"

"I told you, no." Thornton backed to the door and closed it, his gun still held in his right hand.

"How'd you get in?"

"The door was open."

Steinberg looked around, shaking his head.

"I want my money," said Thornton.

"What money?"

"The money you took from me. The five thousand."

"That was my money."

"I want it."

"I don't have it anymore."

"I want it, Steinberg."

"Come and get it then." He stood with his feet apart, his hands beckoning to Thornton.

"I'm not playing games," said Thornton. "I want it." He cocked the hammer on the gun. His hands were shaking. "I want that money."

Steinberg studied Thornton, especially the shaking hand with a cocked gun.

"All right. It's in my pants pocket."

"Take it out slowly and throw it to me. On the floor."

"OK." Steinberg took out the small packet of money and threw it carefully at Thornton's feet. Thornton bent and lifted it, the gun still pointed at Steinberg, his eyes still on him.

"There's no five grand in here."

"That's what's left. I blew it."

"Empty your pants pockets."

"OK."

Steinberg emptied them and showed him his wallet. It contained just a few bills.

"Now, take off your jacket."

"Look, that's what I have."

"Take it off. I'll shoot, I swear it. I want my money." His voice was high-pitched, almost a scream.

Steinberg took off his jacket and held it in his hands. "Now what?" he asked Thornton.

"Throw it low, at my feet." Steinberg did just that. Thornton rummaged through the jacket with his free hand, patting the pockets, and found the other cash packet.

"You didn't have it, heh? You didn't have it?" His eyes were full of rage. Steinberg instinctively backed off. "I ought to kill you. Kill you." Thornton screamed the last words.

Steinberg watched his face, not moving.

"Now, turn around," said Thornton.

Steinberg turned.

"Take off all your clothes."

"What is this?"

"Take them off."

When Steinberg was naked, Thornton shoved him into the bedroom, closed the door, and then ran out of the apartment, still holding the gun, which he tried to shield with his jacket. He didn't know how to uncock the hammer. He ran to his car, gunned the motor, and sped away.

34

"I'm Carl Anderson; so good to meet you."

"Good meeting you," said Milner, as the men shook hands in his office.

"And I want you to call me Carl, all right?"

"Fine."

"All right, Harry. I hate formality. Now, I want you to meet my team. This is my personal assistant, Bob Grove, and this is my comptroller, Pete Dobbs."

Milner shook hands with the two men. It was noon on

Sunday, and the men had just arrived from Cleveland. Anderson was tall, about six foot four, very slim, with broad shoulders and an athletic body. He was in his fifties, completely bald, and what little hair he had around his ears was clipped short. His eyes dominated his face and were icy blue.

The other two men were much shorter. Dobbs resembled a British officer, with a clipped mustache and erect bearing. Grove was the youngest of the three, and looked as though he had played football at an Ivy League college ten years before.

"I've never seen a clock like that," said Anderson, pointing to Milner's wall clock.

"You don't see them much outside of Las Vegas. It not only shows me the time, but reminds me of the odds. Both hands are now on twelve, which pays 30 for 1 at our craps tables. The correct odds are 35 to 1."

Anderson chuckled. "Always thinking of business. I like that. Let's see the casino, Harry. I've never been in a casino before, and I'd like you to point out whatever is of interest."

"OK, let's begin the tour."

They left the office and went out into the casino. Anderson walked alongside Milner, with the two other men following close behind.

He first showed them the cashier's cage.

"This is the heart of our credit operation," Milner said. "Notice the three cameras in the room. They're on all the time."

"Who's watching the TV screens?" Anderson asked.

"Most of the time, Chet Gardner or his assistant. Or Moe Lewis, who's casino manager, or myself. The cameras are there mostly as a deterrent, because the people in the cage have been with this hotel for a long time and are completely honest. I'd vouch for everyone in the cage.

We're not plagued with shortages the way some other casinos are."

"Are there many forged chips?" Grove asked.

"Why do you ask?"

"That sign." He pointed to a notice next to the cage stating that, because of recent forgeries, the El Capitan wouldn't accept chips from other casinos.

"Well, that's not really true. The Strip hotels have banded together and decided to cash in only their own checks. We do it to control our bankroll. It gives us a line on who's playing and who's winning. And if checks are taken from us dishonestly, they have to bring them here to cash them. It's a good control for us and every other Strip hotel."

"Interesting," said Grove.

"It's protection. There's a big cash flow here and we protect ourselves any way we can."

From the cage, they walked to the baccarat pit. It had just opened, and several young women were sitting at the table, talking to the tuxedoed dealers.

"The women at the table are shills, or starters, as we call them," said Milner. "It's difficult to get a game going in the afternoon, but we have a lively baccarat game evenings. That table makes us close to a million dollars a year in profits."

"Really," said Anderson, going to the rail and looking over the table. "From this one table?"

"Yes. And if business continues to pick up, we're looking for a million and a half this coming fiscal year."

"Well, lead on, Harry."

"This is craps. We expect close to a million in profits from each table during the coming year. Our gross, which we call the drop, and our win, which we call our hold, are both on the increase."

The men stood away from a crowded table, packed with

shouting players, then moved to craps 6, which wasn't being used.

"This is called a layout," explained Milner, pointing to the green felt surface. "We usually have five employees at each table. Three dealers, and two boxmen. The boxmen watch the dealers; the stickman, who's a dealer and calls the game, watches the boxmen; and our floormen—the men in suits standing in the pit—watch everybody, the dealers and the players."

"What does C E stand for?" Anderson asked, bending over and closely looking at the layout.

"Craps, 11. All these bets in the center are called proposition bets, and range in profit for us from 6 to 17 percent. We're glad to take all proposition bets."

They passed the roulette tables, only one of which was in operation. Two women were at the table, betting with yellow and red checks.

"Roulette, as you can see, isn't very popular here. Or in any of the casinos."

"Why is that, Harry?"

"Because we have a zero and double zero, and thus our edge on all bets is 5.26 percent. Smart gamblers don't want to buck those odds. In Europe it's a popular game because they have only a single zero and the *en prison* rule, which makes it a better game for players. Still, we take in almost $200,000 a year from each table."

He coughed, and lit another cigarette, closing his eyes for a moment. His head spun. He'd gotten only four hours sleep last night, and the turmoil of the events yesterday still was with him. His hands were clammy as he lit the cigarette.

"And here, we have blackjack," Milner continued. "It's also called twenty-one. We use four decks dealt out of a shoe. We used to have a single-deck game, but there are several advantages for us in the four-deck game. We have a bigger edge, the game is faster, and the players never touch the cards, which are dealt open. If they can't touch them, they can't mark or palm them, or add cards to the deck."

"You're really security-conscious," said Dobbs.

"We're very security-conscious. We have to be."

They were now at the keno lounge.

"This is a great little money-maker for the casino. We take in $700,000 now and should be doing better next year. We have about a 20 percent edge on the players at keno. And now we come to the slot machines. Wonderful money-makers, because they need little supervision. All we need is a slots manager, a slots mechanic, and two change girls. The machines do the rest." He blew out some smoke. "Any questions?"

"No, not now, Harry," said Anderson.

"Anything else you'd like to see now?"

"No."

"Like to have some lunch? We can eat in the restaurant. They have fine food. Or you can go to the suite of rooms I've reserved for you and eat there."

"Let's go up to the rooms," said Anderson. "And we'll just have some coffee, Harry. We ate lunch on the plane coming in."

In the suite upstairs, the men sat over their coffees, waiting for Anderson to speak. He sat serenely, however, his eyes half shut, his mind seemingly a thousand miles away. Milner watched the chairman of the board and chief executive officer of Consolidated Franchises closely, wondering what he was thinking about.

Milner closed his own eyes again. God, he needed a rest. He opened them when Anderson began to speak.

"Harry, I've been impressed by what you've shown us, really impressed."

"Thank you."

"Right now, our lawyers in Detroit are waiting for my call. If I say yes, they'll meet with Mr. Balofsky tomorrow and sign the necessary papers. I must say, though, I've never dealt with a man like Mr. Balofsky before."

Milner lit another cigarette.

"And I'm impressed with the El Capitan. I like a business that generates a good cash flow. Cash is a good commodity to have. It's like any other commodity and costs money. But I guess you understand that?"

Milner nodded.

"Mr. Balofsky spoke highly of you, and we know what you did for this hotel. We've seen the figures. You almost doubled the gross business of the El Capitan."

"After this month, it *will* be doubled."

"Wonderful, and you know the casino business inside out."

"I've been in it for almost thirty years now. Started from the bottom as a dealer."

"I like to hear that," said Anderson. "That's the American way, the American dream. I began as a short-order cook in Columbus, Ohio, so I know what you're talking about. We have something in common."

Anderson drank the rest of his coffee and put down the cup.

"Yes, Mr. Balofsky spoke highly of you. And, Harry, I'm going to take this plunge into Las Vegas. I like this business. I like the numbers and I like the whole setup."

"I think it's a wise move on your part, Carl."

"I think so, also. It feels right, and when something feels right, it *is* right." He leaned back and stretched his long legs out. His shoes were black and highly polished.

"Do you know much about our business, Harry?" he asked.

"Franchises? No."

"It's not only franchises now. We own a can company,

a meat-processing plant; we even manufacture tennis rackets. We're diversified, and we function well, because we're a team, and if I must say so, a damned good team."

Milner listened closely, shifting his weight in the chair.

"When we take over a new business, we put our team to work. Of course, we respect the men running the business; they're the experts and we're not. But we still adhere to the team concept. We know the men on our team. They've stood the test of time."

Milner ground out his cigarette.

"So, if we take over here, and I'm sure there'll be no trouble with the Gaming Commission approval of our license, we're going to work the same concept. We'll put our team in charge."

Milner said nothing, leaning back in his chair.

"Now, Harry, I can see you're ready to ask me, what about me? Very well. I have a proposition for you." Anderson drew in his long legs and sat erect.

"Here it is. We realize that the casino is the heart of this operation, and we know you're one of the best men in the business. We want you to continue to run the casino."

"The casino?"

"Yes."

"You mean, as casino manager?"

"If that's what the position is called, yes."

"Moe Lewis is our casino manager now."

"Yes, we know of him. He's old, Harry. And he has unsavory things in his past. We've checked out all the executives here."

Milner coughed; it was a harsh, hacking cough. Finally, he was able to clear his throat.

"You mean, I'd no longer be president of this hotel?"

"Harry, I thought I just made that plain. We'd be putting our own men in charge. We have a team image. You'll become part of our team, and, in time, you'll have your day in the sun. We expect to buy other hotels; we're nego-tiating in Wichita and in Omaha. You'll have a hotel to run, don't worry."

Milner stood up.

"I've been in this town for close to thirty years," he said. "It took me that long to get where I am now, and you sit there and think that with a few words, you're going to tell me to go back to a place I was five years ago. Do you know what you're telling me?"

"It'll only be temporary. After we purchase the other hotels, I'm sure you'll be running one of them. Just be a little patient with us."

"I have roots here, Carl. What do you want me to do, go to Omaha? Are you serious?"

"Now, Harry . . ."

"No. There's no way I'm leaving this city, and there's no way I'll be casino manager here. No way."

"Harry, think it over . . ."

"Forget it. Enjoy your stay here. I better get down to the floor."

He walked to the door. The men remained seated, watching him.

"Harry, think it over. Don't rush into—"

Milner slammed the door behind him. He walked down the corridor, his body feeling hollow and empty. Maybe if he were less tired, he could argue with the bastard. But not now. In the elevator, he started coughing hard and had to put a handkerchief to his mouth. He walked through the casino in a trance and headed for his office. Moe Lewis was outside his door.

"What happened?" Moe asked.

"They offered me your job. They want me to be casino manager."

Lewis stared at him, chewing on a dead cigar.

"That's what the fucker offered me. Can you believe it?"

"What'd you say?"

"What do you think, Moe? What do you think I said?"

He went into his office, sat down and leaned back in the chair, swiveling it from side to side. Milner picked up the phone and called the Denver number. Still no answer. He slammed down the receiver. That was finished, his marriage. He wouldn't go through this again, calling like a fool, day and night. He'd move her goddamn things out of the house.

He had to get away from Vegas for awhile, think things out. Everything was getting to him. When he had called Shapiro that morning and told him about Steinberg's returning the money, Shapiro said he had the same luck with Teddy and the drug dealer, Manny Franks. They had gotten back 100 G's, and Shapiro told Milner he and his boys were flying back to Detroit that day.

Milner could imagine the pressure they had put on the dealer. Was it any different from the pressure he had put on Steinberg? That threat against Diane . . . why was he so involved with her? Why had he bothered with Steinberg? If he had told people what he had done, they'd tell him he was crazy. A Strip hotel president putting himself on the line like that. Crazy.

He recalled Steinberg's last look. Utter contempt for him. For the second time in his life, he couldn't look someone in the eyes.

It was no good. It was all no good.

Shapiro, Panetta, Balofsky . . . with them it was money, money, and more money. Money was everything to them. You burned them out of their fucking money and they went nuts.

Well, he had done his part in getting them back their lousy money. He'd done his part well, degrading himself the way he had this morning. What the hell, Milner thought, it was better that he got to Steinberg before those others did. Before Panetta did. They were capable of any-thing. Anything.

Anderson and his vultures were smoother, but they didn't seem any better. Team image. What about what he had accomplished at the El Capitan? What about the re-spect he was due for the job he'd done? Team image, shit.

It was no good. None of it was any good. And the worst thing was, he was tied to this town. He was settled here, chained here. There was no way he could leave Vegas now.

The phone rang. It was Chet Gardner.

"Harry, I've been trying to get you. Mike English is in my office."

"What's happening?"

"He's tapped out, and wants to see you right away."

"He's tapped out? Give him a message from me, would you, Chet? Tell him I told him to go fuck himself. And I don't want to see him. If he comes into this office, I'll throw him out of the hotel personally. Tell him that."

"Harry, what's the matter?"

"Never mind. Just tell him that, Chet."

Milner sat at his desk and poured himself a shot of Scotch. He gulped it down, but it didn't help. He had an-other. Then he pushed the glass and bottle away and sat silently, staring at the far wall.

Above him, the clock showed the time, 1:50. The long hand was on the hard 10, paying 8 for 1, and the short hand, the hour hand, moved inexorably toward 2, snake eyes, craps, a loser on the pass line.

35

After Thornton left Steinberg's apartment, he drove down Flamingo Road, feeling a wild surge of excitement and power that he had never experienced before. He had just broken the law; he had taken a $45 investment and with guts had turn it into thousands.

It was time to take off for California, and he headed for the Interstate Highway. But at the MGM Grand he suddenly pulled into the parking lot. He was hungry, and it would be wise to get something to eat before setting off on his long trip.

He parked in the rear, hiding the car behind a camper. The thought that Steinberg had called the police troubled him and excited him at the same time. No, he thought, Steinberg wouldn't call the cops. It didn't seem logical that he would; he didn't seem the type. But you never could tell.

He walked rapidly along the side of the building, where the Jai Alai games were held, and into the back entrance of the Grand.

Thornton took the escalator up to the main floor and stopped in the delicatessen, taking a seat at the counter. He ordered ham and eggs and drank down a couple of cups of coffee. He ate quickly, left a tip and paid the check, and was soon out the door and on his way to the nearby casino.

He decided just to look over the action, then leave, get in the car and head for LA or perhaps San Diego. He'd have to remember to fill up the car with gas, but he could do that on the Strip.

Thornton walked casually past the gaming tables, feeling the money burning in his pocket as if it were aflame.

As though pulled by a magnet, he stopped at a craps table, and decided to play just the contents of the smaller packet of cash. Win or lose, that would be it, and he'd be on his way.

He took out the roll of bills and counted it for the first time. Two thousand exactly. What a bonus. He dropped the money down and received four stacks of green quarter checks.

The point was 5, and a roller was in the middle of his shoot. While this was going on, he took out the other packet and counted it, fingering the cash, moving the edges. There was five thousand there. Plenty of reserve. By the time he finished counting the cash, the roll was over.

Thornton started betting conservatively, $50 on the pass line, and $50 more on the place numbers. Soon he was in the hole for a thousand, and within a half hour, the two thousand was gone. Time to go. Get out of there. The remembrance of that night of horror at the baccarat table was still with him, but today, he thought, was different. He just felt lucky. Hadn't he been lucky getting that money from Steinberg? He still had his five grand intact.

Thornton went to another table, cashed in the whole pile, taking black casino checks, $100s, and betting big right from the start. Before he knew it, it was all gone. The dice were cold, ice cold. It was all gone. He could feel his body turning numb, as he emptied his wallet, taking out $40, all that remained, and betting $10 each on the hardways.

The shooter had a hundred on the pass line and had all the numbers covered with black checks. The roller was a tall man wearing a western hat and western shirt with string tie, and had hard blue eyes and a lantern jaw. He shook the dice fiercely. The point was six.

"Come on, you lovely big red six," the roller shouted in his high Texas twang.

"Seven, line away," said the stickman.

Thornton was wiped out. Now he was really busted, out on his ass and on his feet. He staggered away from the table, not wanting to think, trying to close down his mind. He pushed his way past people, unseeing, unfeeling. A blinding pain shot through his temples, like an electric charge.

Outside, he found the car with difficulty. The sun was beating down, and the heat felt unbearable after the coolness of the casino. He got in and drove out on Flamingo, crossing the Strip.

He found himself on Interstate 15, heading for LA. Cars shot by as he drove at twenty-five miles an hour, completely drained, out of it. He could feel his eyes filling with tears. *What have I done? What have I done?*

Near Jean, about eleven miles down the road, he was too exhausted to go further. Thornton pulled the car onto the side of the road, letting it drift on the hot, barren desert sand. The air inside the car was suffocating. He hadn't even turned on the air-conditioner or opened the windows.

"Mama, forgive me," said Lee Thornton in the closed stopped car. "Mama, I've been bad, forgive me."

He started to cry as he took the gun out of the glove compartment. It was still cocked. He looked at the dark weapon and closed his eyes, feeling the tears stinging as he did so.

"Oh, mama, I've been so bad," he said, as he put the gun to his right temple, waiting, waiting for the last sound he'd ever hear.

36

It took Steinberg no more than an hour to pack his things into two suitcases. He was leaving with about what he had come to town with. He wouldn't take the TV set or the radio; they had been smashed. He'd leave a lot of things. If he had to, Steinberg thought, he'd go with the clothing on his back and the picture of Paula.

It was time to blow out of this town, out of goddamn Vegas. Get the hell out, even though he hadn't gotten his stake after all. All he had left were some of the traveler's checks he had saved; so in effect he was coming out even. Well, it was something.

Just looking around the shambles of his apartment was enough to persuade him to leave. But now he wasn't even sure of where he wanted to go. It would have been nice to get back to New England or upstate New York and look at some land. But he was in no position to become a land-owner now. He had barely enough to last him for a few months on the road.

The road was there. It would always be there. He'd get on it and see where it led. He'd wind up somewhere, try to start fresh, get some kind of work.

Steinberg carried the two suitcases out the door, closing it for the last time, not even wanting to look back at the broken furniture, at the wrecked apartment. It held no real memories for him anyway; it was just another place to stay, another place to crash, to sleep, to have a drink or a meal in.

The Pontiac was parked in the back, and fortunately it was intact. The bastards might have wrecked it as well, and without a car, where would he be? He opened the trunk and shoved in the two suitcases. He felt the spare tire. It had good rubber and was solid. He walked around the car and looked over the tires. They, too, were in good shape. He was ready for a long trip now.

He was sweating from the effort of carrying the suitcases down. The sun was sinking on the horizon, but the heat was awful. Steinberg got into the car and started the motor, letting the air-conditioning come on. It would take a few minutes before the car cooled off.

While sitting in the driver's seat, he thought of Thornton. That bastard . . . but what could he do? Thornton had blown with his money, but everything evens out. Everyone gets paid back in the end. He thought of his own life, of Paula dying on the hospital bed. He got paid back himself, didn't he?

And what about Paula? Didn't she get paid back? What bad things had she ever done? She got it anyway. Maybe it wasn't so, maybe you didn't get paid back. Maybe you just got it for living. And, if you were a good person like Paula, you got it faster for trying to make someone else's life beautiful.

He didn't even want to think about things like that. In his mind he was back where he started from, leaving New Jersey less than a year ago, leaving everything and nothing. And he was alone again.

The car had cooled off. He backed it out of the parking spot and cut through the alley onto Twain. He headed east, toward Boulder Highway, which led to Kingman, Arizona, on Route 66. Go back the same way he came.

As he drove along, Steinberg thought of Diane. He had treated her like shit for a long time, and yet he knew he liked her. He liked her a lot. All he could ever think about was that she was a chip hustler, but what the hell was he? A gambler. An outcast.

Why had he always felt so superior? Just because she had a struggle she could handle only in her own way?

Well, she tried. And the point was, she had a good heart. She had always been kind and gentle to him. Jesus, she had tried, and he had stepped all over her.

Why? He couldn't think clearly. Maybe it was his own insulation, the feeling that he had his personal suffering—his memory of Paula—to sustain him. But how long could you live like that?

Now he was running away again, the same way he ran from the East. He was heading for that long cruel highway, for nights alone in cheap motels with green walls, for days fighting the road himself, and then, when he got to the East, he'd still be nowhere.

That's where he'd be, nowhere. Where would he go to settle down? He was just tired of it all, tired of living alone. He had held himself together for a long time, but it was time to let go a little. He needed a woman, someone to share things with, someone to talk to. Diane wasn't Paula; no one would be like her. But Diane was her own person.

At Boulder Highway in Henderson, he stopped at an Arco station and went to the phone booth and dialed Diane's number. She got on after the first ring.

"Hi, Don," she said, "where are you?"

"I'm in Henderson."

"In Henderson? Are you leaving town now?"

"I was going to, but listen, I was thinking . . ." He hesitated, wiping his face with a handkerchief. The booth was stifling. There was a long silence as she waited for him to continue. "I was thinking about what you were saying, Diane, you know, about us being lucky together. You still feel that way?"

"I don't know anymore, Don. Every time I talk to you, it's like talking to a stone wall."

"I know. I know." He wiped his face again. "But I've been doing a lot of thinking myself."

"So have I," said Diane. "Are you sure you want to take a chance with me?"

"If we don't take the chance, we won't know, will we?"

"No, I guess not, baby. We won't know."

"Well, I'm driving back to Vegas now. We can talk things over. What do you say?"

"I'll be here waiting for you, Don."

After he hung up the phone, Steinberg went back to the car and turned on the motor. He let the cool air of the air-conditioner bathe his face and body. Then he turned the Pontiac around and headed back toward Vegas.

The sun had sunk behind the mountains in the west, and the night was coming on, the wild dark desert night. Steinberg had never gotten used to that night, but now, in the car, heading back to Diane, he felt comforted by its presence.